INTRODUCTORY PSYCHOLOGY IN DEPTH: BIOLOGICAL TOPICS

INTRODUCTORY PSYCHOLOGY IN DEPTH: BIOLOGICAL TOPICS

Wayne H. Holtzman, Editor
University of Texas

Jan H. Bruell
University of Texas

Gerald H. Jacobs
University of California, Santa Barbara

Charles S. Watson
Boys Town Institute for Communication Disorders in Children, Omaha

HARPER'S COLLEGE PRESS
A Department of Harper & Row, Publishers
New York, Hagerstown, San Francisco, London

Cover photo: Michel Craig

Sponsoring Editor: Paula White
Project Editor: Karla Philip
Designer: Michel Craig
Production Supervisor: Kewal K. Sharma
Compositor: American Book–Stratford Press, Inc.
Printer and Binder: The Maple Press Company
Art Studio: J & R Technical Services Inc.

INTRODUCTORY PSYCHOLOGY IN DEPTH: BIOLOGICAL TOPICS

Library of Congress Cataloging in Publication Data
Main entry under title:
Introductory psychology in depth.
  Designed to be used with Introductory psychology by W. H. Holtzman.
  Includes bibliographies.
  CONTENTS: Bruell, J. H. An introduction to human behavior genetics.—Jacobs, G. H. How we see.—Watson, C. S. Hearing.
  1. Psychology.   2. Psychobiology.   I. Bruell, Jan H. An introduction to human behavior genetics. 1978.   II. Jacobs, Gerald H. How we see. 1978.   III. Watson, Charles S. Hearing. 1978.   IV. Holtzman, Wayne H.   V. Holtzman, Wayne H. Introductory psychology.
BF121.I565   152   77–11061
ISBN 0-06-168414-7

CONTENTS

A common complaint in the introductory course is that too many topics are covered in too superficial a manner for the student to have any real understanding of what psychology is all about. Psychology is such a large and rapidly growing field that no single introductory textbook can give the student more than a passing acquaintance with the many interesting ideas and new discoveries concerning the mind and human behavior. General textbooks always represent compromises that fall short of satisfying the majority of students and teachers who have established their own priorities as to what should be emphasized or ignored in the introductory course. Introductory Psychology in Depth *is a series of books designed to overcome this problem.*

Many instructors want to stress the social aspects of human behavior to a greater degree than the typical coverage of an introductory textbook, while others prefer to emphasize the biological nature of psychology. Still other instructors and students want to delve more deeply into selected topics concerned with the growth and development of the individual in family and society. Such a choice is possible with one of these three books as a supplement to the standard introductory textbook. Social Topics *contains four units—"Aggression and Violence," "Interpersonal Processes," "Small Group Processes," and "Attitudes, Opinions, and Persuasion."* Biological Topics *consists of three units—"Human Behavior Genetics," "How We See," and "Hearing."* Developmental Topics *has four units—"The Family and Primary Groups," "Psychological Assessment," "Behavior Disorders of Childhood," and "Drugs and Human Behavior."*

Each unit is written by a recognized specialist who has also achieved a reputation as an outstanding teacher. These particular units were chosen because they deal with timely topics of considerable interest and importance that are rarely treated adequately in the introductory textbook. Although carefully coordinated in style and level of difficulty, the units can be studied individually in any order. While designed specifically for use with Introductory Psychology, a basic textbook published by Harper's College Press, these three books are well suited to supplement any introductory text where greater depth in biological, social, or developmental topics is desired.

Biological Topics begins with an introduction to human behavior genetics, a rapidly growing field in psychology. While the inheritance of behavior in man has been a subject of much speculation and some research for at least a century, only recently have new methods been applied which combine modern genetics, statistics, and psychology. Unit One is longer than the others because it cuts across several areas of science that must be understood in order to gain any real insight into how they are joined together in the relatively new field of human behavior genetics. The author of this unit, Dr. Jan H. Bruell, is professor of psychology at the University of Texas at Austin.

Unit Two deals with our visual system and how we see. Beginning with the physical and anatomical basis for vision, the reader moves on to the sensitivity of the eyes in responding to various stimuli and the nature of color vision. The unit concludes with a brief discussion of binocular vision, eye movements, and motion. The author of this unit, Dr. Gerald H. Jacobs, is professor of psychology at the University of California, Santa Barbara.

Unit Three deals with another essential sensory system, hearing. The importance of both hearing and vision to an understanding of the mind and human behavior is self-evident. The unit begins with a brief introduction to the physics, physiology, and anatomy of the ear as a basis for understanding the psychology of hearing itself. Sensitivity in detecting a sound, discriminating among sounds, masking, loudness, pitch, and timbre are presented with special attention to methods of psychoacoustic measurement. How sounds are localized in space, the nature of speech, deafness, and noise complete the unit. The author, Dr. Charles S. Watson, formerly professor of psychology at Washington University and senior research associate at the Central Institute for the Deaf, is now director of research at the Boys Town Institute for Communication Disorders in Children.

Wayne H. Holtzman

INTRODUCTORY PSYCHOLOGY IN DEPTH: BIOLOGICAL TOPICS

AN INTRODUCTION TO
HUMAN BEHAVIOR GENETICS
UNIT ONE

JAN H. BRUELL
University of Texas

GENETIC CONCEPTS

Behavior genetics is about one hundred years old. Throughout the ages inquiring minds must have wondered about inheritance of behavior in man; but the first major printed work on the subject was Francis Galton's (1822–1911) book, *Hereditary Genius, an Inquiry into Its Laws and Consequences,* published in 1869. In the preface to the 1892 edition of his pioneering treatise (p. 25), Galton wrote:

> At the time when the book was written, the human mind was popularly thought to act independently of natural laws, and to be capable of almost any achievement, if compelled to exert itself by a will that had a power of initiation. Even those who had more philosophical habits of thought were far from looking upon the mental faculties of each individual as being limited with as much strictness as those of his body, still less was the idea of the hereditary transmission of ability clearly apprehended.

Today, one hundred years later, many still believe the human mind acts independently of natural laws and inherited physical constraints. Most people accept the reality of eye color genes, skin color genes, genes for stature, genes for obesity, and so on. But genes for behavior are another matter. Most of us find it hard to believe that genes constrain and control our behavior.

No two people behave alike; individual differences in behavior are undeniable. Some people are quick in all they do; others are slow. Some are inventive; others rarely come up with an original solution to a problem. Some have a pleasant nature; others are abrasive and hostile. Is such inequality acquired, as it is widely believed today, or is it innate? Galton's Victorian contemporaries viewed it to be the result of personal choice, a view Galton vehemently rejected (Galton, 1892, p. 56):

> I have no patience with the hypothesis occasionally expressed, and often implied, especially in the tales written to teach children to be good, that babies are born pretty much alike, and that the sole agencies in creating differences between boy and boy, and man and man, are steady application and moral effort. It is in the most unqualified manner that I object to pretensions of natural equality.

Deep in our hearts we find the idea of inherited inequality with its implied innate shackles on our freedom repugnant. But such emotional reaction aside, what are the facts? Are the agencies creating differences between individuals "steady application and moral effort", the environment into which destiny has cast us, or genes passed on to us in egg and sperm by our parents? These, stated in simplest form, are the central questions of behavior genetics.

Behavior genetics, as the name implies, is part psychology and part genetics. It uses the language of geneticists, and it is almost impossible to talk about its findings in any other language. We, therefore, place a glossary of genetic terms at the beginning of this discussion. Intensive study of the glossary is not necessary at this point. But the reader should become sufficiently familiar with its contents to be able to refer to it as the need arises.

GAMETES

Every cell of sexually reproducing organisms descends in direct line from parental reproductive cells or *gametes*. It descends from an egg (*ovum,* pl. *ova*) contributed by its mother and a sperm cell contributed by its father. The study of so-called *instinctive* behavior shows that gametes can carry and transmit information about behavior. Consider, for example, the case of salmon. The female salmon releases her eggs into the water where they are fertilized by sperm released by the males and both parent fish die soon after the reproductive act. When the young that develop from the fertilized eggs later behave as their parents did, we deal with an impressive instance of inheritance of behavior. The parents could not have instructed the young in the ways of salmon. They could pass on to them information about behavior only by one route: they must have transmitted it in their gametes, their egg and sperm cells that united to form the primordial cells of their offspring.

CHROMOSOMES

Chromosomes and genes. Egg and sperm are the vehicles carrying genetic messages from parent to offspring. But where in those cells are messages encoded? Gametes contain threadlike structures that are readily colored by a variety of stains used in the preparation of microscopic slides. The structures, therefore, have been called "colored bodies" or *chromosomes.* Thousands of carefully designed experiments with plants and animals have proved that chromosomes are involved in the transmission of genetic messages. More specificly, research has shown that chromosomes consist of a series of macromolecules of *DNA* (*deoxyribonucleic acid*), the elementary material units of heredity. These molecules of DNA are called *genes,* and they are the bearers of hereditary information.

Chromosome number in somatic cells. We distinguish between reproductive cells or *gametes* and *somatic cells,* the name given to all cells of the body that are not gametes. In somatic cells, chromosomes occur in pairs. The members of a chromosome pair carry identical or similar genetic material and are, therefore, said to be *homologous*. The number of chromosome pairs found in somatic cells is constant within a species, but varies from species to species. For example, in somatic cells of fruit flies we find four pairs of chromosomes. Horses carry 32 pairs of chromosomes in their somatic cells, and the somatic cells of man contain 23 pairs. If we designate the number of chromosome pairs in a cell by the letter N, then the number of chromosomes in that cell is 2N. In fruit flies 2N = 8, in horses 2N = 64, and in man 2N = 46.

Chromosome number in gametes. Somatic cells contain 2N chromosomes; but gametes, ova and sperm cells, contain only N chromosomes. Thus gametes have only half as many chromosomes as somatic cells; they are said to have a *haploid* set of chromosomes. By contrast, somatic cells are said to contain a *diploid* set.

Zygotes. Sperm and ova are haploid cells. When a sperm unites with an ovum, the product of the union, the fertilized egg, is a diploid cell. This primordial diploid cell of every multicellular organism is referred to as *zygote*. By extension of its meaning, zygote also refers to the individual that develops from the fertilized egg.

Autosomes and sex chromosomes. The diploid chromosome set of man consists of 46 chromosomes. Two of the 46 chromosomes are intimately involved in the determination of sex and are, therefore, called *sex chromosomes;* the remaining 44 chromosomes are called *autosomes.*

In females, the two sex chromosomes, called X chromosomes, are alike. In males, the two sex chromosomes differ: males have one X chromosome and one Y chromosome. In genetic shorthand, the chromosomal constitution of females is 46,XX; and the chromosomal constitution of males is 46,XY.

CELL DIVISION

Mitosis. All cells of a multicellular organism descend from the fertilized ovum or zygote. The zygote divides into two daughter cells, these divide again, resulting in four cells, and so the process continues. The human body is made up of billions of cells, all descended by division from the primordial zygote. The process of division by which somatic cells multiply their number is called *mitosis*.

The essential features of mitosis are that in the process all chromosomes of the mother cell are duplicated and that each of the two daughter cells receives a complete set of these chromosomes. All somatic cells of the body contain identical chromosomes, and all of them are exact copies of the chromosomes the parents supplied in their gametes.

Meiosis. Ova and sperm cells contain N rather than 2N chromosomes. They are haploid cells, but they descend from diploid precursor cells, called *oogonia* in females and *spermatogonia* in males. The process of cell division that divides diploid oogonia and spermatogonia into haploid gametes is called *meiosis.* During meiosis the two homologous members of each chromosome pair separate, each homologue becoming part of a different haploid gamete.

The essential feature of meiosis is that in the process *each gamete receives one and only one member of a chromosome pair.* Each diploid precursor cell, *D,* divides into two gametes, *G1* and *G2.* If D contained a chromosome pair (1/1′), then meiosis can be represented by formula

$$D(1/1') \longrightarrow G1(1) \text{ and } G2(1')$$

THE HUMAN KARYOTYPE

We mentioned that during mitosis each chromosome is duplicated. The process becomes clearly visible during one phase of mitosis, the *metaphase,* when the duplicates of each chromosome, called *chromatids,* come to rest side by side, held together at one short region known as *centromere.* As mitosis proceeds, the sister chromatids are seen to separate, one moving into one and the other into a second daughter cell.

At metaphase the chromosomes—actually paired chromatids— have the appearance of a bow, or letter *X;* and it is usually at this stage that photomicrographs of chromosomes are made (see Figure 1). The chromosomes are photographed through the eye piece of a microscope, the microphotograph is enlarged, prints are made, and the pictures of individual chromosomes are cut out from the print. The chromosomes are then arranged in a standard way, resulting in what has come to be called the karyotype of an individual.

Figure 1A shows the karyotype of a human male. Shown are "metaphase" chromosomes. Autosomes are arranged in pairs, grouped according to size, and numbered from 1 to 22. The sex chromosomes, X and Y, are labeled. As can be seen, each chromosome appears to be split lengthwise into identical halves, the chromatids. The chromatids have not yet separated, being held together at the centromere.

Since 1970, new techniques of karyotyping have been developed. When these new techniques are used, chromosomes take up stain in a pattern of dark and light bands. Each pair of chromosomes

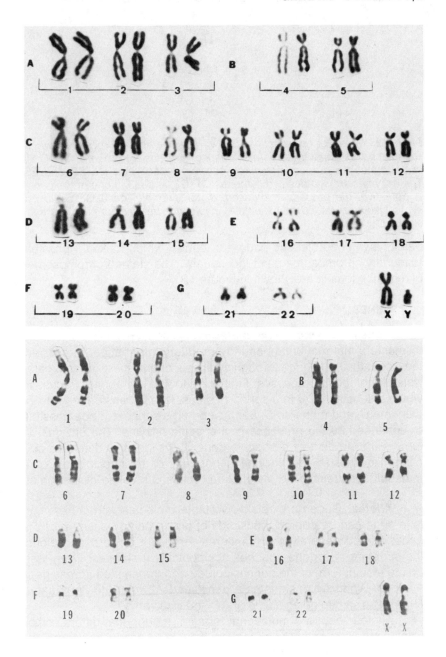

Figure 1. *Karyotype of human female (top) and male (bottom).*
A. Conventional preparation of chromosomes at the metaphase stage of cell division. Shown is the karyotype of the human male. B. G-banded (Giemsa-banded) preparation of chromosomes of human female. [Karyotypes courtesy of David Ledbetter, Austin State School.]

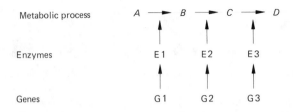

Figure 2. *Model of gene action. Shown is a metabolic process in which substance A is transformed into substance D. Steps A→B, B→C, and C→D in the metabolic process are made possible by enzymes E1, E2, and E3. The enzymes are synthesized by genes G1, G2, and G3. If one of the genes is defective, the process is blocked. If, for example, gene G3 could not synthesize enzyme E3, substance C could not be transformed into substance D.*

has its own characteristic pattern of bands, which makes it possible to identify chromosome pairs individually. The stained chromosomes of a human female are shown in Figure 1*B.*

GENES

Genes, enzymes, and metabolic processes. Genes are the elementary material units bearing hereditary information. In general, they exert their influence through synthesis of *enzymes,* organic catalysts of *metabolic* processes. Figure 2 shows a metabolic process in which a substance *A,* in a series of steps, is first transformed into *B,* then into *C,* and then into *D.* Each step in the series is made possible or enhanced by the presence of a specific enzyme. The enzyme, in turn, is the product of a specific gene. If the gene is defective and cannot synthesize the enzyme necessary for a specific step of a metabolic sequence, the metabolic process is blocked at that point.

Alleles. Genes are relatively stable molecular structures; that is, a gene can be copied thousands of times, being passed on from generation to generation in unaltered form. But on rare occasions, the structure of a gene changes accidentally; it *mutates.* From then on the mutant form of the gene is copied and transmitted across generations. When *A1* designates a gene, and *A2* refers to its mutated form, *A2* is said to be an *allelle* of *A1,* and vice versa.

Alleles, then, are mutational forms of a gene that differs somewhat in structure and hence function. If allele *A1* produces an enzyme E1, then *A2* produces another enzyme E2, or it produces no biologically active enzyme at all. That is, E2 may have a different catalytic action than E1, or it may have no catalytic, reaction-enhancing function.

It is customary to designate allelic forms of a gene by similar symbols, for example, *A1* and *A2, A* and *A', B* and *b,* and so on.

Chromosome loci of genes. Today it is firmly established that genes are located on chromosomes. Like beads on a string, genes are linearly arranged along the length of each chromosome. The position of a gene on a chromosome is relatively fixed. If three genes *A1, B1,* and *C1,* are located on a chromosome in this order, the location of gene *B1* will tend to remain between gene *A1* and gene *C1* from generation to generation. Thus each gene has its chromosome *locus* (*plural, loci*), that is, a definite position in the linear order of genes residing on the chromosome.

Alleles occupy homologous chromosome loci. If allele *A1* occupies locus *A* on one member of a chromosome pair, then allele *A2* occupies locus *A* on the other member of that pair.

Sex-linked genes. Both autosomes and sex chromosomes carry genes. Genes whose locus is on the X chromosome or Y chromosome are said to be sex-linked.

ZYGOTES

Homozygotes and heterozygotes. Chromosomes occur in pairs. An organism carrying the same form of a gene on corresponding loci of homologous chromosomes is said to be a *homozygote.* Using symbols, *AA, bb, C1C1, D2D2* are homozygotes. On the other hand, organisms carrying allelic forms of a gene on corresponding loci of homologous chromosomes are called *heterozygotes.* For example, *Bb, Gg, H3H4, LL'* are heterozygotes.

Genes and genotypes. We distinguish between genes and genotypes. *A1* and *A2* designate genes or alleles; but *A1A2* designates a *genotype,* the genetic constitution of an individual or zygote. Assume an egg carrying alleles *B1* and *C1* unites with a sperm bearing alleles *B2* and *C1.* The resulting zygote will be of genotype *B1B2 C1C1.* It will be heterozygous at locus *B* and homozygous at locus *C.*

PHENOTYPES

The term *phenotype* has the same root as the term *phenomenon,* which denotes an event or fact directly perceptible to the senses. Geneticists use the term phenotype to refer to any observable, measurable characteristic or trait of an individual. Eye color, skin color, blood type, stature, weight, heart function, lung capacity, and digestion of an individual are examples of morphological and physiological phenotypes.

Psychologists are primarily interested in behavioral phenotypes, that is, observable, measurable, characteristic forms of behavior an individual displays. A person's performance on an intelligence test is a behavioral phenotype; and so is his rating on a personality test, his ranking in class, his characteristic ways of attacking and solving problems, his sociability or aggressiveness, his ability to think clearly, or his deluded thinking that led to his hospitalization in a psychiatric institution. All these are behavioral phenotypes.

GENOTYPES AND PHENOTYPES

Geneticists use many terms to describe the relationship between genotype and phenotype. Here we will explain six such descriptive terms, namely, recessiveness, dominance, pleiotropy, monogeny, polygeny, and chromosomal anomaly.

Recessiveness and dominance. Certain kinds of deafness are caused by an allele at a locus *D.* Individuals whose genotype is *dd* are deaf-mute, but *Dd* heterozygotes and *DD* homozygotes have normal hearing. Note the difference between the effects of the *d* and the *D* alleles on phenotype. Allele *d* causes deafness only when present in double dose, that is, in the *dd* homozygote. When present in single dose in the *Dd* heterozygote, allele *d* has no effect on phenotype: it escapes notice, it recedes into the background, it is *recessive.*

By contrast, allele *D* causes normal hearing whether present in single dose in the *Dd* heterozygote, or in double dose in the *DD* homozygote. It dominates the scene in either case; it is *dominant.* Considering the *Dd* heterozygote only, we can say that in it *D* is dominant over *d,* or that *d* is recessive to *D.*

Pleiotropy. Many genes have more than one phenotypic effect. Even genes with a clear-cut major effect, such as deafness, may have diverse secondary effects. Genes with multiple effects often underlie what medicine calls a "syndrome," the "running together" of clinical signs. In 1965, for example, Nyhan, Oliver and Nesch described a syndrome caused by a sex-linked recessive gene. The gene causes mental retardation and compulsive self-mutilation by gnawing of lips and fingers. Other manifestations of the gene are excessive excretion of uric acid in the urine and gouty arthritis with recurrent disabling inflammation of joints. Thus Lesch and Nyhan's gene has several distinct phenotypic effects, some behavioral, some biochemical, some physiological and morphological. Genes with multiple phenotypic manifestations are said to have *pleiotropic effects* or to be pleiotropic.

Monogeny and polygeny. It is useful to distinguish between *monogenic* and *polygenic* traits. Genetic analysis of a trait often reveals that it is affected primarily by the action of a single gene at one chromosome locus. Some forms of deafness, as described earlier, and Lesch-Nyhan's syndrome are examples of such single-locus, monogenic traits. With existing genetic methods, monogenic traits are particularly easy to study. We will deal with such traits later.

Most traits of interest to psychologists are caused not by a single gene with major, easily detectable effects, but by the joint action of many genes, each of which, taken singly, has only a minor phenotypic effect. Traits caused by the additive action of many genes with small effects are called *polygenic* traits.

Chromosomal anomalies. Behavioral abnormalities are sometimes caused by abnormal sets of chromosomes rather than mutant genes. For example, in 1942 H. Klinefelter, an American endocrinologist, described males with small testes, enlarged femalelike breasts, and a variety of behavioral abnormalities. Later it was found that such males have an extra X chromosome—they are 47,XXY males. The study of individuals with chromosomal anomalies is progressing rapidly, and we will discuss various behavioral effects of abnormal chromosome sets in the next section.

CHROMOSOMES AND BEHAVIOR

Behavioral geneticists study the dependence of behavior on the chromosomes and genes residing in every cell of our body. The most direct evidence for such dependence is supplied by individuals with abnormal sets of chromosomes. Chromosomal abnormalities can be seen under the microscope, and it is thus often possible to say whether an individual has a normal or an abnormal set of chromosomes. In recent years, it was found that in many cases chromosomal abnormalities predispose to abnormal behavior; and we will report some of these findings. We will discuss, in order, anomalies of autosomes and sex chromosomes and will see that, in general, the former tend to lead to more severe behavioral disturbances than the latter.

autosomes worse than sex-somes

ANOMALIES OF AUTOSOMES

Down's syndrome. According to present estimates about one in 700 of all newborns and about ten percent of all persons in institutions for the mentally retarded have Down's syndrome, so named after Langdon Down, a British physician who first described it as a separate clinical entity in 1866. Down noticed in the patients facial features reminiscent of the physiognomy of certain Mongol peoples; and he, therefore, called them mongols or mongoloids. We shall use the terms Down's syndrome and mongolism interchangeably.

It would be hard to find a person who has not heard of mongolism or met a child or adult afflicted with it. Mongolism is a major health problem, but fortunately, because of newly gained genetic knowledge, we can hope to gain a certain measure of control over it. Patients with Down's syndrome are of interest to us because most of them are mentally retarded.

Morphological and functional abnormalities. Down's syndrome is characterized by a large number of morphological and functional abnormalities. Practically every organ system of the body is affected, but no two patients manifest exactly the same set of symptoms. The head of patients tends to be small, short, and flat in the back. The face is roundish; the nose has a low bridge. The oral cavity is too small for the tongue, which may protrude from the open mouth. The eyes slant upward toward the outer corners which contributes to the somewhat Mongolian appearance of the patients. Adult patients are rarely taller than five feet. Many patients are myopic or have other visual disorders (Figure 3). Cardiac anomalies and leukemia are common.

Intelligence. Mongoloid babies are branded at birth by their visible defects, and many are institutionalized right then because of pessimistic prognoses physicians often offer to the parents of the infants. But what are the facts? First, the danger of diagnostic labeling must be stressed. Not all mongols are alike; each is an individual with his own potentials and limitations that unfold gradually and cannot be ascertained at birth. Most institutionalized mongols have an intelligence quotient (IQ) below 50 and, as adults, hardly ever a mental age above seven years. But samples of institutionalized cases tend to be biased, and there is reason to believe that among patients living with their families, many have IQs of 60 to 70. The average mongoloid child learns to walk late, at about two years, and often starts to talk even later. Yet many mongols are in the educable range, capable of benefiting from instruction through the first two or three school grades.

Exceptional cases. The literature contains reports of several mongols whose intellectual attainments were unusual. The intelligence of one patient, a Mr. Bolt, was tested when he was over 40. On a vocabulary test he could define "recede" and "espionage," and on a test of general knowledge he unhesitatingly replied "Goethe" when asked who wrote *Faust.* Another patient has published a 12,000 word diary of his childhood, *The World of Nigel Hunt,* a most unusual document (see Box 1). The patient typed his own

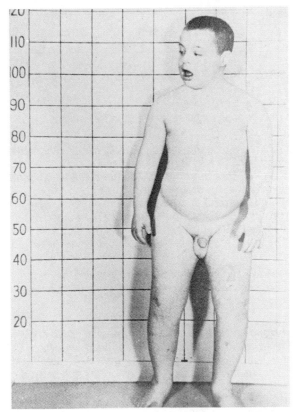

Figure 3. Down's syndrome. The clinical features are mental retardation, a peculiarity in the folds of the eyelids suggesting the eyes of Mongoloid peoples (although in fact quite different), a small roundish head and face, an oral cavity too small for the tongue, short stature, stubby hands and feet, peculiarity of the palm prints, and congenital malformations, especially of the heart. [From Victor A. McKusick, Medical Genetics 1958–1960 (St. Louis: The C. V. Mosby Co., 1961). Reproduced by permission.]

manuscript, and it contained only a few spelling errors. The authenticity of the manuscript was confirmed by the English geneticist L. S. Penrose, who contributed greatly to the study of Down's syndrome and who knew the patient personally. In a preface to the diary, Penrose gives credit to the unusual capabilities of Nigel, and points to the concreteness of his thinking. Nigel reproduced faithfully what he experienced; he described his experiences as a child would describe a picture. He did not generalize from a concrete event to a class of similar events, did not form abstract concepts; and his ability to use

---

BOX 1

EXCERPTS FROM THE DIARY OF A MONGOL

Nigel grew up at home where he received most of his education. He could read reasonably well by the time he was six:

> My mother has been so kind to me all my life. My mother taught me to read. When I was very tiny we used to play together with plastic letters and a book with huge letters in it. I learnt the sounds of the letters from my mother as we played.
> After I had learned the sound of every letter mother held things up and sound-spelt them like "This is a C-U-P" and soon I could do it all by myself; all our friends were amazed and pleased with me when I began to read properly from books (Hunt, 1967, pp. 97–98).

In the following passage Nigel recalls one of his adventures. He had left home by himself to watch a "Trooping of the Colour" at Buckingham Palace:

> So I stood and waited for at least one and a half minutes. I heard a terrific throb and my ears were lifted and with a Biff bang the band came along, and when they turned the corner up came their oompahs and the miserable trombones and blowed me in the middle of nowhere (Hunt, 1967, pp. 54–55).

Excerpted from Nigel Hunt, The World of Nigel Hunt. New York: Garrett Publications, 1967.

---

number concepts was particularly impaired (Sarason and Doris, 1969).

Social maturity. While intellectually most mongols never outgrow early childhood, socially they become maturer. They can care for themselves; and many observers have emphasized their affectionate, good-natured manners, their friendliness and even their sense of humor. There is some exaggeration in this positive characterization of the personality of mongols. Not all mongols are friendly or affectionate, but controlled studies indicate that young mongols are remarkably "normal": they run no greater risk of developing an emotional disturbance than other children. And when institutionalized mongols were studied, they showed signs of emotional disturbance less frequently than the retarded group as a whole (Silverstein, 1964).

Summary of psychological findings. To summarize the psychological findings, the label "mongol" given to a newborn infant often conjures an unduly pessimistic prognosis. Parents expect that their child will never learn to walk or to talk and that it must be institutionalized right away. The opposite expectations can also arise: having heard of the "prince charming" nature of some mongols and believing in the limitless potential of modern methods of "behavior modification," parents are apt to set too high goals for their child. In the majority of cases, the truth lies probably in between. Like children, patients with Down's syndrome depend on the sheltered environment provided by adults. But they are *trainable,* that is, they learn to take care of their personal needs; and they are *educable,* that is, they benefit from elementary instruction. Individual differences are pronounced, and how trainable and educable a patient will be cannot be foretold at birth. Most outstanding is the fact that the chromosomal aberration that causes mongolism limits the intellectual growth of patients more than it limits their emotional and social development.

Genetics of Down's syndrome. Until 1959 the cause of mongolism was a complete mystery. Mongols are much more often born to mothers late in their child-bearing years than to younger women. This fact suggested various environmental causes of mongolism, most of them speculative, but nevertheless widely accepted. It was believed that older women have a "worn-out" reproductive system, one spoke of "mother-exhaustion," and one suggested that mongolism was a developmental disorder: an abnormal prenatal uterine environment caused abnormal development of the child. Other environmental causes of mongolism were advanced. The condition was blamed on infection by syphilis or tuberculosis, on alcoholism, on contraceptives, on psychiatric conditions, and on epilepsy. It was seen to be caused by various hormonal deficits, including abnormalities of the adrenals, the pituitary gland, the thymus gland. It was thought to be caused by a thyroid deficiency, and patients were treated with thyroid extract. In spite of this diversity of opinion, three facts appeared established:

1. The risk of mongolism increased with maternal age (Table 1.1)
2. On occasion, mongolism appeared *heritable;* that is, it reoccurred in several generations of a family, and some parents had more than one affected child.
3. In cases of heritable or familial mongolism, the age of the mother played a minor role. In fact, the risk of a young

TABLE 1.1 RISK OF DOWN'S
SYNDROME AS A FUNCTION OF MATERNAL AGE

AGE OF MOTHER	RISK OF MONGOLOID CHILD
0–34	1 in 700
35–39	1 in 300
40–44	1 in 100
45–49	1 in 50

mother to have a second mongol was much greater than that of a mother whose first affected child was born late in her reproductive years.

These facts became understandable when in 1959 three French geneticists (Lejeune, Gautier, and Turpin, 1959) discovered that patients with Down's syndrome are *trisomic* for chromosome 21, having 3 rather than the usual 2 chromosomes number 21. The picture was further clarified when soon thereafter it became known that trisomy can be of two kinds: "simple" trisomy 21 and translocation trisomy 21 (Slater & Cowie, 1971).

Trisomy 21. Trisomy 21 is a consequence of abnormal meiosis. Gametes are formed by meiotic division of a diploid oogonium or spermatogonium. Considering chromosome pair 21 only, a diploid cell can be represented by symbol $D(21/21')$. Meiosis divides $D(21/21')$ into two gametes, each containing one 21-chromosome:

Normal meiosis:

$$D(21/21') \longrightarrow G1(21) \text{ and } G2(21')$$

On rare occasions meiosis miscarries. The members of a chromosome pair do not separate, resulting in two abnormal gametes, $G1$ and $G2$:

Abnormal meiosis, non-disjunction:

$$D(21/21') \longrightarrow G1(21/21') \text{ and } G2(-)$$

If gamete $G1(21/21')$ is fertilized by a normal gamete $G(21)$, a trisomic zygote is formed:

Trisomic zygote:

$$G1(21/21') + G(21) \longrightarrow Z(21/21' + 21)$$

TABLE 1.2 MODEL OF FORMATION OF
GAMETES AND ZYGOTES IN TRANSLOCATION TRISOMY 21

GAMETES PRODUCED BY TRANSLOCATION CARRIER D (14 + 21/14, 21/−)	ZYGOTES PRODUCED BY UNION OF THESE GAMETES WITH GAMETES OF FORM G (14′, 21′)	FATE OF ZYGOTE
G (14 + 21, 21)	Z (14 + 21/14′, 21/21′)	Mongol
G (14 + 21, −)	Z (14 + 21/14′, −/21′)	Carrier
G (14 , 21)	Z (14/14′, 21/21′)	Normal
G (14 , −)	Z (14/14′, −/21′)	Monosomia 21 nonviable

And if gamete $G2(-)$ is fertilized by a normal gamete, $G(21)$, a monosomic, also abnormal zygote results:

Monosomic zygote:

$$G2(-) + G(21) \longrightarrow Z(21)$$

The risk that during meiosis chromosome pair 21 does not
separate and hence the risk of a trisomic mongoloid child, increases
with maternal age, as shown in Table 1.1. Monsomic zygotes, $Z(21)$
are nonviable and are aborted before term. We do not know why
meiotic accidents increase with maternal age. No satisfactory theoretical explanation of the phenomenon is as yet available. The risk
figures discussed are *empirical risk figures;* they are based on statistics rather than deduced from theory.

Translocation trisomy 21. It has been observed under the
microscope that during cell division a chromosome sometimes gets
attached end to end to another chromosome, remaining permanently
joined to it. In the case of mongolism, there appears to be a special
affinity between chromosome 21 and chromosome 14, or 15, or 22.
Suppose then that chromosome 21 attaches itself to chromosome 14,
resulting in diploid oogonia, spermatogonia, and somatic cells of
form $Z(14 + 21/14, 21/-)$. Carriers of such a translocation of chromosome 21 to chromosome 14 can live normal lives because their
cells remain essentially disomic: they contain two chromosomes 14
and two chromosomes 21. But what happens when a carrier of such
a *balanced translocation* produces gametes? And what happens
when these gametes unite with normal gametes? A model of these
events is given in Table 1.2.

TABLE 1.3 EMPIRICAL RISK OF DOWN'S SYNDROME IN OFFSPRING OF CARRIERS OF TRANSLOCATIONS

PARENT	OFFSPRING		
	NORMAL	CARRIER	MONGOL
Empirical risk			
Female carrier	50/100	40/100	10/100
Male carrier	39/100	59/100	2/100
Theoretical risk	1/3	1/3	1/3

In theory, counting viable offspring only, carriers should have $1/3$ normal, $1/3$ carrier, and $1/3$ mongol offspring. Fortunately, the empirical risks, particularly for male carriers, are smaller than the theoretical risk figures would indicate. Empirical risk figures for female and male translocation carriers are given in Table 1.3). The difference between theoretical and empirical risk figures can be partly attributed to prenatal loss of a certain proportion of trisomic fetuses. About 15 percent of all pregnancies end in spontaneous abortion, and 35 percent of fetuses aborted spontaneously during the first 120 days of pregnancy have chromosomal abnormalities. Those trisomics that are carried to term and are born are presumably the most viable among the many more that are conceived, but aborted. Let us note that no satisfactory explanation exists for the sex difference shown in Table 1.3.

Counseling in mongolism. It is useful to distinguish between *premating, prenatal,* and *postnatal* counseling. With respect to mongolism, consider the most common case: a mongoloid child is born and the parents seek postnatal counseling. They want to know whether the child should be committed to an institution, or in case he remained with the family, how to train and educate him. In such circumstances, psychologists are often consulted. Almost unavoidably problems falling in the area of premating counseling come up: should the parents avoid having another child? A prenatal counseling problem arises if the mother becomes pregnant again: what are the chances for her to carry another affected baby?

Implicitly we have talked about postnatal counseling already. At the time of birth an accurate prognosis about the behavioral potential can rarely be made. If the family can carry the heavy burden, it is certainly to the child's advantage to stay in the family where its development can be closely watched permitting a more informed decision at a later date. Nigel's parents (see Box 1) recall that when their mongol son was born, they were told that no amount of love and care lavished on Nigel would help: Nigel would remain an uneduca-

BOX 2

SAMPLE PEDIGREE

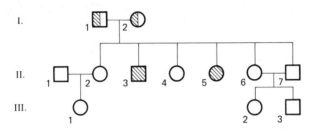

Sample pedigree.

Data on human inheritance are often presented in the form of pedigrees. The pedigree reproduced above shows three generations, indicated by Roman numerals I, II, and III. Males are represented by squares, females by circles. "Marriage lines" connect individuals I-1 and I-2, II-1 and II-2, and II-6 and II-7. A "sibship line" connects individuals 2 to 6 in the second generation and the sister-and-brother pair in the third generation.

Individuals II-3 and II-5 possess the trait whose inheritance is being studied. This is indicated by filling in the square and circle. Hollow circles and squares show nonaffected individuals. Half-filled circles and squares (see I-1 and I-2) are often used to represent heterozygous, nonaffected carriers of a condition.

The pedigree is characteristic of an autosomal recessive disorder (see also Box 4). The grandparents I-1 and I-2 are presumably heterozygous carriers of the disorder studied.

ble idiot. Nigel's father comments, "If we had accepted this, it would have come true." Nigel's parents did not listen; and Nigel's diary shows that, thanks to them, he lived a relatively happy life.

Geneticists specialize in premating counseling. Let us see how they go about it. (Before continuing, the reader should study Box 2, which explains the symbols used in pedigree charts.) Suppose that in the family depicted in Figure 4 the girl III-4 is a mongol. She was born when her mother was 37 years old. What are the chances that her parents will have another affected child?

Case 1. Because of the advanced age of the mother and the fact that III-4 was her first abnormal child, one assumes that the girl has a simple trisomy 21. The risk of another mongoloid child is considered to be about one in 300; that is, it is judged to be not greater

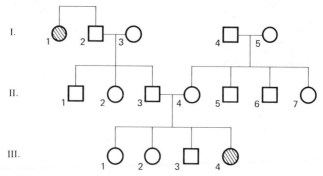

Figure 4. Pedigree of mongoloid child, III-4. The mother, 37 years old, is not a carrier of a translocation. A paternal aunt, I-1, had Down's syndrome. What is the risk of female III-4's having another mongoloid child?

than for any other mother of that age (see Table 1.1). To make sure, the patient is karyotyped. She has indeed three chromosomes 21, which reinforces the prognosis.

Case 2. The prognosis again is based first on maternal age. However, when the child is karyotyped, it is found to be a translocation trisomic. Thus it becomes important to determine whether the father or the mother is the translocation carrier. If the father is the carrier, the risk of another abnormal child is two in 100, but if the mother contributed the translocation, the risk increases fivefold to ten in 100 (see Table 1.3). Actually, in both cases, the risk is somewhat larger because of the maternal age factor.

The possibility that the father is the translocation carrier is considered first because a check of his family reveals that his aunt, I-1, was a mongol. The father's karyotype, however, is found to be normal. Subsequent karyotyping of the mother shows that she is normal, too! This suggests that the translocation arose anew when the paternal gamete was formed. Chances that the same rare event would reoccur in one of the parents is small. The risk of another mongol child is one in 300; it is primarily a function of maternal age.

Prenatal counseling is sought if there are grounds to suspect that the unborn child is abnormal. In the case of mongolism, it is possible to confirm or eliminate the suspicion by the procedure known as *amniocentesis.* The fetus develops in a fluid-filled sac called *amnion.* The amniotic fluid contains some cells that are derived from the fetus itself. During amniocentesis, the amnion is punctured with a needle and some amniotic fluid is withdrawn. Cells contained in the fluid are cultured and used for diagnosis. A trisomia can be detected that way. If the feared diagnosis is made and it is determined that the child has Down's syndrome, the parents face the agonizing ethical decision of whether to terminate the pregnancy. But as a recent pamphlet of the National Institute of Child Health and Human Development on "Antenatal Diagnosis and Down's Syndrome" (DHEW Publication No. 74–538) points out:

> *The most significant benefits are those perceived by couples facing a "high-risk" situation who, without the availability of amniocentesis, might needlessly choose to interrupt pregnancy. One case concerned a 31-year-old mother of a two-year-old child with Down's syndrome (Trisomy 21), who discovered that she had become pregnant again. After she learned that she had approximately a one percent chance of producing another child with mongolism, she demanded an abortion. Her physician suggested that she undergo amniocentesis and prenatal chromosome analysis first, to determine whether or not the child would be affected. She agreed, and much to her relief, discovered that the fetus had a normal karyotype. The mother decided to complete the pregnancy and eventually delivered a normal baby.*

OTHER ANOMALIES OF AUTOSOMES

We discussed trisomy 21 at some length because it is a common anomaly. There exist other trisomic conditions involving autosomes, for example, trisomy 13 and trisomy 18. But these conditions are rare and so severely disabling that most affected children die very early. We will, therefore, not deal with them here.

ANOMALIES OF SEX CHROMOSOME NUMBER

Anomalies of sex chromosomes are more common than anomalies involving autosomes, and fortunately, they are by and large less debilitating. In this section we will describe three conditions caused by abnormal numbers of sex chromosomes, namely, the Turner, Klinefelter, and XYY syndrome. We will also discuss a recent study of unusually long Y chromosomes in criminals.

Turner's syndrome: 45,X females. About one in every 2500 girls is born with only one X chromosome, thus having a 45,X chromosomal constitution. The chromosomal defect causes a host of anatomic and physiological anomalies, collectively referred to as Turner's syndrome. Patients often are dwarfed in stature, being usually under five feet. They have a webbed neck (see Figure 5), a broad, shield-like chest with widely spaced nipples; and their secondary sexual characteristics develop slowly. In fact, many patients come to the attention of physicians because, at the age of puberty, they fail to menstruate. Examination then reveals that the girls do not have

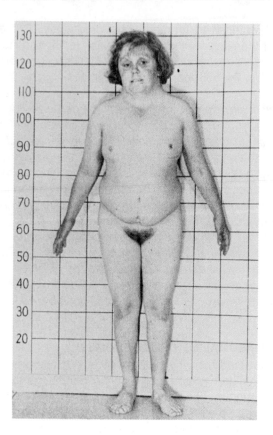

Figure 5. *The Turner syndrome. The features are female external genitalia, short stature, webbed neck, low-set ears and typical facies, broad shield-like chest with widely spaced nipples and undeveloped breasts, small uterus, and ovaries represented only by fibrous streaks.* [*From Victor A. McKusick* Medical Genetics 1958–1960 (*St. Louis: The C. V. Mosby Co., 1961). Reproduced by permission.*]

ovaries and thus do not produce the sex chromosomes that cause normal feminization of the body during adolescence.

Girls and women with Turner's syndrome show few signs of psychopathology. On the contrary, John Money (1975), professor of medical psychology and pediatrics at The Johns Hopkins Hospital, who has studied a large number of Turner females, marvels about their extraordinary mental health. He attributes this to an "inertia of emotional arousal" manifested by many of the patients. Although stigmatized by their short stature and various other visible anomalies, the patients tend to face life with a high degree of equanimity. According to Money, "In Turner's syndrome, one has an example of the genetics not of psychopathology, but of psychologic health" (Money, 1975).

Turner patients are of major interest to psychologists because of a cognitive disability Money discovered in them. On intelligence tests a sample of 45,X females does not differ greatly from a sample of normals; but closer examination of the test performance of individual patients reveals a discrepancy between their "verbal intelligence," which often is above average, and their ability to visualize space. To the extent that tasks involving spatial relations form part of a standardized intelligence test, the overall score obtained by the patient is lowered. We will return to this interesting finding later.

Klinefelter's syndrome: 47,XXY males. Boys with a 47,XXY karyotype, like girls with a 45,X chromosome set, tend to come to the attention of physicians during adolescence and for similar reasons. The normal bodily changes expected to occur during puberty are delayed; and when virilization of appearance does take place, it is often incomplete and inadequate. The testes are small and in most cases, incapable of producing sperm; the pubic hair grows in a female distribution; and in some cases femalelike breasts develop (Figure 6). The syndrome was first described in 1942 by Klinefelter after whom it is named. Originally, because of the abnormal development of sexual characteristics of 47,XXY males, endocrine anomalies were considered to be the primary cause of the various manifestations of the syndrome.

Table 1.4 shows the incidence of the 47,XXY karyotype in three populations: newborns, psychiatric patients, and institutionalized retardates. The difference between the incidence of 47,XXY males in neonates and institutionalized individuals points to an association between the 47,XXY genotype and various behavioral disabilities. Many investigators have studied Klinefelter patients; and although findings differ somewhat from study to study, the following picture emerges.

As to intelligence, all levels of intelligence are represented among XXY males, but their average IQ is below the population average of 100. Also, as Table 1.4 shows, about five times as many XXY males are among the mentally retarded than in the population at large. However, usually the retardation of those committed to institutions is not profound.

Various personality disorders are found among institutionalized retarded and psychiatric XXY patients. A high proportion of adult XXY males who find their way into psychiatric institutions or homes for the retarded get there because of participating in antisocial behavior such as larceny, fire setting, indecent exposure, and so on. No one behavioral aberration appears to predominate; but it is clear that XXY males, when compared to chromosomally normal males, have a heightened risk to manifest socially deviant behavior.

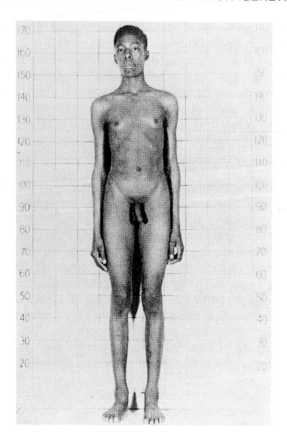

Figure 6. The Klinefelter syndrome. The external genitalia are of male type but the testes are consistently very small and body hair is sparse. Most of the cases have gynecomastia—female-like breast development. Patients tend to be unusually long-legged. [From Victor A. McKusick Medical Genetics 1958–1960 (St. Louis: The C. V. Mosby Co., 1961). Reproduced by permission.]

Finally, it must be stressed that there are certainly many XXY males in the general population who never come to the attention of psychiatrists, psychologists, social workers, or officers of the law. These XXY males presumably lead relatively normal lives.

The 47,XYY syndrome. In 1965, five British investigators (Jacobs et al, 1965), published a paper entitled "Aggressive Behavior, Mental Subnormality, and the XYY Male." The stated intent of the paper was "to report our findings in a survey of mentally sub-normal male patients with dangerous, violent or criminal propensities in an institution where they are treated under conditions of special secur-

TABLE 1.4   FREQUENCY OF 47,XYY
MALES IN DIFFERENT POPULATIONS

POPULATION	INCIDENCE
General population at birth	2 in 1000
Psychiatric patients	7 in 1000
Institutionalized retardates	10 in 1000

ity." Jacobs's report was given wide publicity by the press; and soon, in the mind of the public, the XYY karyotype was linked to violent criminality. When in 1966 in Chicago Richard Speck murdered eight nurses, the press reported that Speck was an XYY male, a claim that turned out to be wrong, but continues to influence popular notions about XYY males. A sober evaluation of the data now available leads to a much less extreme picture.

Jacobs suggested an association between the XYY karyotype and mental subnormality, but such an association was not clearly established; average and even high IQs are compatible with the genotype. As to criminality, Table 1.5 shows that XYY males are indeed overrepresented in prison populations. Overrepresentation is particularly striking in institutions for mentally disturbed offenders, pointing to a causal relation between the XYY karyotype and delinquent and deranged behavior. However, the original suggestion that XYY males commit predominantly violent crimes against persons and thus must be held "under conditions of special security" has not been confirmed. With regard to crimes of violence, XYY males do not differ from XY males. In fact, while in prison, XYYs show less aggressive behavior than do XY prisoners. Most crimes of XYY males are directed against property rather than persons (Witkin et al., 1976). Those XYY males who get into conflict with the law—and only a minority of them do—tend to have a long history of deviant behavior. According to Money, they are difficult children, have problems in school, are given to excessive daydreaming, are loners and drifters, have unrealistic expectations for their future, are impulsive and prone to sudden violence and aggression. Indeed, Money regards impulsiveness to be the core difficulty of XYY individuals: they are not good at self-regulation of behavior. Ordinarily, lack of self-control is characteristic of childhood and early adolescence; in XYY males, immature behavior tends to carry over into early adulthood.

Length of Y chromosome and antisocial behavior. We discussed studies of 47,XYY males and the suggestion that their supernumerary Y chromosome predisposes them to antisocial behavior. Recently, the role of the Y chromosome with regard to impulsive and

TABLE 1.5 FREQUENCY OF 47,XYY
MALES IN DIFFERENT POPULATIONS

POPULATION	INCIDENCE
General population, at birth	1 in 1000
All male prisoners	3 in 1000
Male prisoners, 6 feet or taller	20 in 1000

sometimes criminal behavior has been studied also in 46,XY males. Johannes Nielsen and Ursula Friedrich (1972), two Danish investigators, obtained karyotypes of 407 males in Danish prisons and of 2000 newborn boys. The relative size of the Y chromosome of each individual was established by measuring the length of the Y chromosome and the length of the F chromosomes (see Figure 1A), and by computing the ratio Y/F. Usually the Y chromosome is shorter than all other chromosomes. F chromosomes, that is, chromosomes 19 and 20, are small, too, but ordinarily, larger than Y chromosomes. Thus only in exceptional cases would one expect the ratio Y/F to be larger than 1.0, an expectation borne out by Nielsen's data: only 1.5 percent of the 2000 newborn boys had Y/F ratios larger than 1.0. But 7.6 percent of Nielsen's 408 prisoners had Y chromosomes that were larger than their F chromosomes.

All male descendants of a male receive his Y chromosome. If a male carried on his Y chromosome genetic material that in some as yet unknown way contributed to antisocial behavior, he would transmit it to all his sons. The brothers would resemble each other and their father. Nielsen used the Y/F ratio to divide males in a prison for juvenile delinquents into two groups: (1) Individuals in the first group had shorter Y than F chromosomes; their Y/F ratio was below 9/10. (2) In the second group the Y/F ratio equaled or was larger than 9/10; they had relatively long Y chromosomes. Nielsen found significantly more criminality and mental illness among fathers and brothers of these delinquents than among those of group 1.

Such findings, if confirmed by carefully designed studies, conducted by different investigators in different countries, would be of major significance. It is generally assumed that a criminal environment breeds antisocial behavior. To most people, the notion of a bad seed is a superstition passed down to us from a less enlightened age. In our time "like father, like son" implies social learning rather than heredity. But if there were only some truth in Nielsen and Friedrich's finding, its implications would have to be considered carefully. In our discussion of mongolism, we already pointed to the danger inherent in the labeling of people. It is hard to imagine what it would do to the psychological development of an individual if, from birth on, he were labeled as an XYY male, or a male with an abnormal Y/F ratio, and if his parents, teachers, and he himself knew that he was at risk to go down the wrong path.

SOME HYPOTHESES ABOUT GENES AND BEHAVIOR

Most individuals have 22 pairs of autosomes and one pair of sex chromosomes; but as we learned in this unit, this is not invariably so. We discussed four relatively common chromosomal abnormalities: the Down, Turner, Klinefelter, and XYY syndromes. We also discussed the recently discovered relationship between the length of the Y chromosome and criminality. The facts we reported show in a direct way that genetic structures affect behavior: different chromosomal constitutions are reflected in different personalities. The relationship between karyotype and behavior is not strong, permitting a great amount of variation; but it does exist; and we must try to understand it. As we develop ideas about the abnormal phenomena discussed here, we will gain a deeper understanding of genetic causes of behavior in general.

To begin, let us note that the genes located on a chromosome, and not the chromosomes themselves, affect behavior. In a trisomic condition, there are too many genes of a kind; in a monosomy, such as Turner's syndrome, there are too few. Abnormal chromosome number leads to abnormal gene number; this, in turn, causes abnormal quantities of gene products, a fact reflected in various abnormalities of anatomy, physiology, and behavior. Different chromosomes carry different sets of genes; and it is therefore understandable that, for example, an extra 21-chromosome in Down's syndrome has other phenotypic effects than a supernumerary X chromosome in Klinefelter's syndrome, or an additional Y chromosome in the XYY syndrome. The abnormal sets of genes in the four syndromes presumably exert their influence on behavior by controlling both the development of bodily structures and the functioning of these structures.

Genes, structures, and behavior. Each of the chromosomal aberrations we discussed is marked by some anatomic abnormality. The abnormal chromosomes cause abnormal growth of the organism. It is unlikely that the abnormal development is limited to readily visible parts of the anatomy. It can be assumed that the proper growth and "wiring" of the nervous system is also affected and that this accounts in part for the frequent association between chromosomal abnormality and mental subnormality.

That genes can cause "miswiring" of the nervous system is well established. Consider, for example, the miswiring of the visual system caused by a gene for albinism. Ordinarily, visual receptors in the retina of the eye are connected by optic fibers to two symmetrically located receiving areas in the brain, the lateral geniculate nuclei. Each eye sends fibers to the geniculate nucleus on the same and opposite side of the brain. Strict spatial order is maintained. If in the retina, receptors A, B, C, D are arranged in this order, then optic fibers A', B', C', D' arrive at the geniculate nucleus in that order. Whether an array of visual receptors connects to the geniculate nucleus on the same or the other side of the brain is also strictly predetermined.

Recently R. W. Guillery and J. H. Kaas, (1973), an anatomist and a neurologist at the University of Wisconsin, demonstrated that in Siamese cats, white tigers, pearl mink, and albino rats the gene for albinism upsets this order. The gene has pleiotropic effects: it not only reduces pigmentation of the fur, but it also affects the crossing of visual fibers. If, for example, in normal animals, fibers A', B', C', D' connect the left eye to the left geniculate nucleus, then in albinos the same fibers cross over to the right nucleus. However, curiously enough, only the side of connection is switched. The order A, B, C, D is not altered, suggesting that alleles of the albino locus determine only whether fibers cross or do not cross; other genes, it seems, maintain the spatial order of optic fiber connections.

Guillery found more: he followed the optic pathways from the geniculate nuclei to the visual cortex and discovered that in albinos some nerve fibers are missing entirely. The miswiring of the visual pathways of albinos has behavioral consequences. For example, many Siamese cats squint.

Not enough is yet known about the anatomy of the nervous system of patients with chromosomal aberrations. Is it possible that in some of them parts of the nervous system become miswired during early development? We mentioned, for example, that patients with Turner's syndrome have normal verbal intelligence but great difficulties with tasks involving visualizations of spatial relations. We know from other research that the ability to imagine spatial relations is related to neurological processes in the right hemisphere of our brain. Could it be that Turner patients have a neurological defect in the right half of their brain? Such a hypothesis may be off the mark, but as more information from diverse areas of genetic, neurophysiological, and behavioral research becomes available, we will learn to formulate better hypotheses. Guillery's studies of the visual pathways in albinos and normally pigmented cats provide an example of one possible mechanism linking genes to behavior: genes affect the structure of the bodily machinery and thus indirectly behavior.

In conditions like mongolism, genes have done their work even before the child is born; and we speak of *congenital defects*. Actually, genes can affect structures subserving behavior, and thus behavior itself, at any time. For example, later in this unit we will speak about phenylketonuria (PKU). In this genetic disorder, phenylalanine, a substance contained in a variety of foods we eat, cannot be converted into tyrosine. Abnormal metabolites of phenylalanine accumulate and poison the nervous system of infants, causing permanent damage. Irreversible mental retardation ensues. It is possible that analogous abnormal, but as yet unidentified metabolic processes occur prenatally in some patients with abnormal chromosome constitutions, leading in them to congenital mental retardation.

Genes, neurotransmitters, and behavior. Some genes affect behavior by affecting the assembly of structures subserving behavior. Other genes affect the functioning of these structures. Primary among them are genes involved in the synthesis of "neurotransmitters." The nervous system is an immense communications network consisting of countless nerve fibers or *neurons* that make contact with each other at points known as *synapses*. Contact is not perfect: neurons are separated from each other by an interneuronal space or synaptic cleft. Communication between neurons is by means of *neurotransmitters,* chemicals synthesized by the neuron itself. Neurotransmitters, released by the terminal of one neuron, cross the synaptic cleft and stimulate receptors at the receiving end of the next neuron. Different neurons produce different neurotransmitters; and brain circuits, assemblies of thousands of neurons, are characterized by specific transmitter substances. Circuits connecting various centers of the brain are intimately involved in the control of behavior. For example, activation of certain circuits by electrical or chemical stimulation elicits aggressive, or sexual, or maternal behavior in experimental animals. In spite of the staggering complexity of the brain processes, they all depend on the relatively simple mechanism of neuron-to-neuron communication by means of neurotransmitters. All modern psychiatric miracle drugs, the various tranquilizers and energizers, exert their profound influence on behavior by influencing interneuronal communication. Tranquilizers work by reducing the amounts of neurotransmitters released into the synaptic cleft or by decreasing the sensitivity of neuronal receptors. Energizers work by increasing the amount of neurotransmitters released or by enhancing the sensitivity of receptors. The effectiveness of psychiatric drugs and the many popular "mind expanding" drugs attest to the major role of neurotransmitters. They control our moods and emotions, affect our level of activity, speed up or slow down, organize or disorganize our thought processes. They truly control our mind and behavior. Evidence is accumulating which suggests that genes exert some of their control over behavior by regulating the synthesis of neurotransmitters. Temperamental differences between individuals, the general sluggishness of some, the excitability and impulsiveness of others, may well be an expression of a gene-controlled, chronic insufficiency or excess of neurotransmitters at junctions of specific nerve circuits of the brain. Because of their impulsiveness, individuals with abnormally long Y chromosomes and individuals with two Y chromosomes are at risk of getting into conflict with the law. It is tempting to speculate that at the root of the behavioral problems of these individuals is an overproduction of certain neurotransmitters, an overproduction possibly caused by genes on the Y chromosome. Research into such matters is rapidly progressing (Axelrod, 1974; Snyder, 1974).

MAJOR GENES AND BEHAVIOR

Behavior genetics studies the relation between the genetic material an individual carries and his behavior. In the earlier part of this unit we learned about one approach to the problem. We classified individuals according to their chromosomal constitution and asked whether differences in chromosomal type were related to differences in behavior. Chromosome analysis is a recent development, since only 20 years ago even the exact number of chromosomes of man was not known precisely. The approach discussed in this unit is much older. In fact, it goes back to 1865 when Gregor Mendel, the father of genetics, published his epoch-making paper on inheritance of various morphological traits in sweet peas.

Mendel crossed peas displaying two forms, T1 and T2, of a trait, and observed in what proportions T1 and T2 appeared in subsequent generations. He noted that one form of the trait often disappeared entirely in one generation only to reappear in subsequent generations in predictable proportions. Based on his observations, Mendel developed a rational model of the underlying hereditary mechanisms. He was the first to suggest that hereditary traits are the visible expression of a pair of "elements" (we call them genes), one of which has come from each parent. Mendel recognized that these elements could differ, and that often only one element affected the trait: one was dominant, and the other was recessive. The model he used permitted him to predict the outcome of specific matings. To the extent that his predictions were borne out by observation, his theory was confirmed and the hereditary transmission of the trait was established.

In this discussion, we will apply the "Mendelian method" to inheritance of behavior. In man, of course, experimental matings cannot be performed; and we must rely on data provided by human families. We study human pedigrees (Box 2) and see whether the appearance and disappearance of behavioral traits over generations show a Mendelian pattern, that is, a mode of transmission predictable from Mendelian theory. If it does, we can assume that the behavioral phenotype studied is the visible manifestation of Mendelian elements or genes transmitted from generation to generation via sperm and ova. In other words, we can assume that there indeed exists a relationship between the genes an individual possesses and the behavior he displays.

Several distinct Mendelian patterns of inheritance are known. How a trait appears and reappears in successive generations depends on the gene causing it. If the gene is located on an autosome, the pattern is different from what it is when the gene resides on a sex chromosome. And if the gene is dominant, the pattern is different from what it is when the gene is recessive. We will present instances of (1) autosomal dominant, (2) autosomal recessive, and (3) X-linked recessive inheritance of behavior. We will also talk about inheritance of schizophrenia, which appears to follow an autosomal dominant pattern of inheritance. Whether it does is still controversial, and we will deal with the controversy.

Before turning to the study of specific instances of autosomal inheritance, the reader should consider the information contained in Boxes 2 and 3. Box 2 (p. 19) explained some of the conventions used in the drawing of pedigrees. Box 3 presents a typical pedigree of an autosomal dominant trait and points to the most important features of autosomal dominant inheritance.

HUNTINGTON'S CHOREA: AN AUTOSOMAL DOMINANT DISORDER

Symptoms of chorea. This autosomal dominant syndrome (see Box 3) was first described in 1872 by George Huntington, an American physician, in an American family of English descent. It is called *chorea* (from the Latin word for dance) because of its most visible symptom, namely, involuntary, uncontrollable jerking movements of legs, arms, and the muscles of the face. The motor disorder is not present at birth, but tends to appear in the early middle age of patients.

Of special interest to us is that frequently the first signs of the disease are changes in the personality of the patient. He becomes irritable, moody, ill-tempered, suspicious, sometimes outright psychotic. Many patients who later were recognized as suffering from chorea, were first committed to a mental institution with the diagnosis of schizophrenia, usually of the paranoid type. In some patients the first changes are in the direction of apathy and depression, often also requiring hospitalization in a mental institution.

BOX 3

AUTOSOMAL DOMINANT INHERITANCE

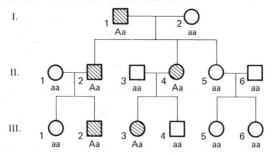

Prototypical pedigree of dominant autosomal inheritance.

Shown is the typical pattern of transmission of a trait caused by a dominant allele *A* carried on an autosome. Illustrated are the following characteristics of dominant autosomal inheritance:

1. Both sexes are affected since the loci of *A* and *a* are on an autosome. Compare this with sex-linked inheritance, Box 5 (p. 41).
2. Only affected individuals transmit the trait. This distinguishes dominant inheritance from recessive inheritance, Box 4 (p. 35). and sex-linked inheritance, Box 5.
3. The trait does not skip generations. Compare this with sex-linked inheritance, Box 5.
4. About one-half of the children of affected individuals are affected, because most matings are of type *Aa* X *aa.* Compare this with recessive inheritance, Box 4.
5. Male-to-male transmission of the trait does occur. Compare this with sex-linked inheritance, Box 5.

The motor disorder appears later. At first the patient seems only nervous and fidgety; but soon movements become recognizably abrupt, jerky, and involuntary. Finally, signs of general mental deterioration become prominent: the patient is unable to concentrate, his thinking becomes incoherent, his memory fades, and he is confused and disoriented.

The behavioral symptoms are related to a progressive degeneration of the brain. Post-mortem examination reveals loss of nerve cells and nerve fibers in various subcortical and cortical areas of the brain, including the frontal lobes. The disease is progressive; there is no known cure for it; and on the average, it leads to death within 12 years after onset.

Pedigree analysis and counseling. Shown in Figure 7 is the pedigree of a family in which chorea occurred in four successive generations. The reader is urged to compare this authentic pedigree of a dominant autosomal disorder with the prototypic idealized pedigree shown in Box 3. There we noted that, in a dominant disorder, generations are not skipped and that only affected individuals transmit the disorder. But how about female II-2 and male III-4 in Figure 7? Female 1-2 died when she was 35. She was not affected herself, presumably because of her early death; but she undoubtedly carried *H,* the dominant gene for *chorea* because she transmitted it to at least two of her children. The same applies to her son III-4. He also died before symptoms of the disease developed in him, but he had two choreic children.

What would a counselor say to female IV-1 if she asked (a) whether she will develop the disease, and (b) what her chances were to pass the allele *H* on to her children? In answer to the first question, one would have to advise her that the initial risk for her having got the dominant gene *H* from her father, an affected male, was one in two, or 50 percent. But then one would consider her age. Statistics show that with 35 years, 22 percent of all patients had shown signs of the disease already. Since she had not, her remaining risk is 78 percent (100 − 22). Combining the two risk figures—that of being a heterozygote and of still developing the disease—one would say that she had a 39 percent ($\frac{1}{2} \times 78$) chance of becoming a victim. With this as premise, her second question can be answered also. The likelihood that a child of hers will receive the gene *H* is one-half of 39 percent, that is, about 20 percent, or one in five.

At present, unfortunately, we have no test that would permit one to diagnose the *Hh* carrier status of an individual before the symptoms of the disease appear. Consequently, children of patients live forever in the fear of succumbing to the disorder; and if they have children themselves, they do not know whether they have passed on the dreaded condition to them. So far, all attempts to develop a test that would distinguish between *Hh* carriers and *hh* individuals have failed. But what if we could distinguish at birth between *Hh* and *hh* individuals? Carriers of the disease would grow up with the terrifying knowledge of their ultimate fate, but the weight put on them would be counterbalanced by the load taken off the mind of their more fortunate *hh* brothers and sisters. The ability to distinguish between *Hh* and *hh* individuals would have an important long-range effect. Most carriers of the allele *H* probably would avoid having children. Under ideal conditions, the disease could be eliminated within one

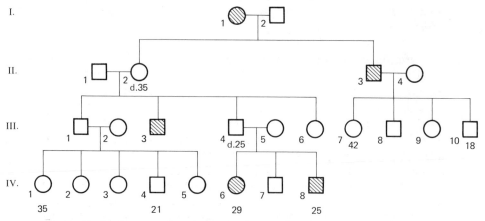

Figure 7. *Pedigree of Huntington's chorea. Current age and age at death of some members of family are given under pedigree symbol. Based on Eliot Slater and Valerie Cowie,* Genetics of Mental Disorders, *Oxford University Press, 1971, p. 146.*

generation, except for the rare spontaneous production of new alleles *H* through mutation.

PHENYLKETONURIA:
AN AUTOSOMAL RECESSIVE DISORDER

Symptoms of phenylketonuria. Better known as *PKU*, phenylketonuria is an example of an autosomal recessive disorder (see Box 4). If untreated, PKU results in severe mental retardation with only a small fraction of the patients having IQs over 70. About one percent of all institutionalized retardates are phenylketonurics. At birth, the infant with PKU is normal. But after a month or two, development is progressively delayed; and at the time most children walk and talk, a large proportion of PKU children does neither. Most of the irreversible brain damage caused by the disease is done during the first 18 months of life.

PKU patients show a variety of behavioral abnormalities. Body movements are often rigid and awkward. In severely retarded patients, an apelike, "pithecoid" gait and stance is sometimes seen. There is a general picture of behavioral unrest and agitation. There are fiddling, contorted movements of hands and fingers; and swinging, rocking motions of the body that can continue for hours. Some patients are hyperactive, noisy and destructive, and have uncontrollable temper tantrums. Some are shy, anxious, and fearful. One observer stated: "None could be described as friendly, placid, or happy" (Omenn, 1976).

BOX 4

AUTOSOMAL RECESSIVE INHERITANCE

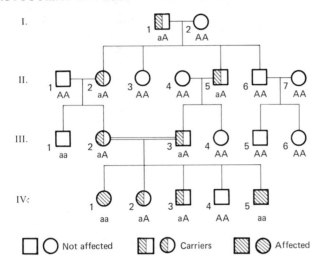

Prototype pedigree of recessive autosomal inheritance.

Shown is the typical pattern of transmission of a trait caused by a recessive allele *a* carried on an autosome. Illustrated are the following characteristics of recessive autosomal inheritance:

1. Both sexes are affected since the locus of *a* is on an autosome. Compare this with recessive sex-linked inheritance, Box 5, where usually only males are affected.
2. Affected homozygotes, *aa;* and unaffected heterozygous carriers. *Aa,* can transmit the trait. Compare this with dominant inheritance, Box 3.
3. Often the parents of affected individuals are blood relatives, for example, first cousins; see pair III-2/III-3.
4. On the average, one-fourth of the siblings of an affected individual are also affected. This is so because most affected individuals result from *Aa* X *Aa* matings. Compare this with dominant inheritance, Box 3.
5. Characteristically, the trait appears in siblings, and not in parents, offspring, or other relatives. Compare this with dominant inheritance, Box 3.

About half of the patients are *microcephalic,* that is, their head is abnormally small. There are many signs of general brain dysfunction. Convulsive epileptic seizures involving loss of consciousness (*grand mal*) and abnormal *electroencephalographic* (EEG) patterns are common. Small epileptic seizures or *petit mal* attacks, characterized by episodes of staring with loss of contact with the environment, are frequently observed. Post-mortem examination of the brain reveals a variety of neurological abnormalities, including a widespread, diffuse *atrophy* of the *cortex.* Normally, nerve fibers are encased in *myelin,* a fatty substance that seems to isolate neighboring fibers from each other. Lack of development or loss of this protective sheathing of nerve fibers is seen in the brain of most PKU patients and may well be one of the primary defects caused by the disease, explaining many of the behavioral symptoms and the abnormal electrical activity of the brain revealed by grand and petit mal epileptic seizures and the EEG.

Metabolic defect. PKU was recognized as a separate clinical entity in 1934 (Knox, 1972; Slater & Cowie, 1971; Omenn, 1976). The father of two affected children noted the peculiar odor of their urine because the smell aggravated his asthmatic condition. The urine was examined by A. Følling, professor of nutritional research at the University of Oslo, who identified excessive amounts of *phenylpyruvic acid* in it. Følling soon found other mentally retarded patients with a similarly malodorous urine and detected that they, too, excreted phenylpyruvic acid. Følling's discovery prompted many biochemical and genetic studies of the disorder, and today the following facts are certain.

PKU is a genetic disorder of metabolism. PKU patients cannot synthesize *phenylalanine hydroxylase,* an enzyme that converts phenylalanine to tyrosine. Thus phenylalanine, contained in a variety of foods we eat, accumulates and is transformed into phenylpyruvic acid. It is this substance that Følling discovered in the urine of patients. Presumably, phenylpyruvic acid, and its metabolites, is also the substance that causes the damage to the developing brain of patients.

Preventive treatment and IQ. Knowledge of the metabolic defect in phenylketonuria suggested a preventive treatment. Phenylalanine is highly concentrated in our normal diet of milk, bread, eggs, meat, and fish. Since PKU infants cannot metabolize phenylalanine, treatment consists of a diet of vegetables and fruit and a special mixture of proteins, all low in phenylalanine. Conscientious adherence to the diet during the first few years of life prevents damage to the brain, the cause of the various behavioral disabilities of

TABLE 1.6 DISTRIBUTION OF IQs IN
TREATED AND UNTREATED PKU PATIENTS

TREATMENT	NUMBER OF PATIENTS	PERCENT OF CASES IN IQ CLASS		
		BELOW 40	40–80	ABOVE 80
Untreated	466	87	12	1
Treated after 16 months	23	70	25	5
Treated before 16 months	20	22	22	56

Source: Data adapted from W. E. Knox, "Phenylketonuria" in J. E. Stanburg, J. B. Wingaarden, and D. S. Frederickson, eds., *The Metabolic Basis of Inherited Disease,* 3rd edition. Copyright 1972 by McGraw-Hill. Used with permission of McGraw-Hill Book Company.

patients. Dietary treatment, however, must be started very early, preferably in the first month of life.

Table 1.6, based on data gathered by Knox (1972), shows the distributions of IQs in three groups of patients. Patients in the first group were not treated, that is, they were never on a diet low in phenylalanine. The second group received dietary treatment relatively late, between the ages of sixteen months and three years. Patients in the third group were put on a proper diet early, most of them before they reached one year of age and all before they were 16 months old. We see that 87 percent of the untreated patients were profoundly retarded, having IQs below 40. By contrast, in the early treatment group 56 percent of the patients had IQs over 80. The group treated late benefited somewhat from the treatment, but not markedly. Clearly, early dietary treatment is essential to prevent irreversible damage to the developing nervous system. To assure early detection and early treatment of homozygotes, several states have passed laws requiring that all infants be tested for excessive levels of phenylpyruvic acid.

Pedigree analysis. The genetic nature of PKU is firmly established. Pedigrees like the one shown in Figure 8 are typical. Comparing this pedigree with the idealized, prototypic pedigree in Box 4, the reader will recognize all the hallmarks of autosomal recessive inheritance. Both sexes are affected. Heterozygotes II-6 and II-7, themselves unaffected, transmit the trait. As is often the case in rare recessive disorders, the heterozygous parents of the patients are blood relatives, in this case first cousins. Finally, the trait appears in siblings and is not represented in other members of the family.

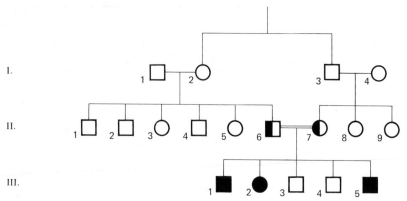

Figure 8. Pedigree of a PKU family. Note the consanguinity of carriers II-6 and II-7. [Adapted from W. E. Knox, "Phenylketonuria" in J. B. Stanbury, J. B. Wyngaarden, and D. S. Frederickson, eds., The Metabolic Basis of Inherited Disease, 3rd edition. Copyright 1972 by McGraw-Hill. Used with permission of McGraw-Hill Book Company.]

Diagnosis of carrier status. PKU patients are unable to synthesize phenylalanine hydroxylase, the enzyme that converts phenylalanine to tyrosine. The enzyme is synthesized by a dominant gene P; PKU patients are homozygous for p, the recessive allele of P. Knowledge of the genetics of PKU suggested a test that permits one to detect heterozygous Pp carriers of the recessive allele p. Unaffected siblings and other relatives of patients can be normal PP homozygotes or Pp heterozygotes. The phenylalanine loading test provides a means of finding out what their genotype is. If PP individuals produce two units of phenylalanine hydroxylase, then Pp individuals produce only one unit of that enzyme. Consequently, if PP and Pp individuals are "loaded" with a meal containing much phenylalanine, PP individuals will metabolize the phenylalanine twice as fast as Pp individuals. Thus if blood samples are taken from PP and Pp individuals at one, two, and three hours following a loading dose, excessive amounts of phenylalanine will be found for a longer time in the blood of Pp carriers than in the blood of PP homozygotes.

Counseling. The *phenylalanine tolerance* or loading test has a place in genetic counseling. Consider, for example, female II-9 in Figure 8. Suppose she wants to marry and, because of PKU in her family, seeks genetic advice. Is she a PP homozygote or a Pp carrier? We know that her younger sister, II-7, is a carrier because she had three PKU children. Without the test for Pp carriers, all we could say to II-9 is that her chances to be a carrier are one in two or 50 percent, because siblings share half of their genes. Today, we need not speak in terms of probabilities. With the loading test, we can determine the genotype of II-9 and tell her whether she is a carrier.

Suppose the test is positive and II-9 is found to be a carrier.

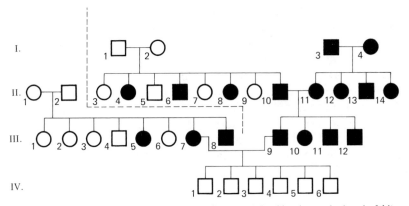

Figure 9. *Deaf-mutism in a family observed in Northern Ireland.* [*After A. C. Stevenson and E. A. Cheeseman,* Annals of Human Genetics, 20 *(1956), 177–231. Cambridge University Press.*]

What are her chances to marry another carrier, assuming she does not marry a relative? The incidence of phenylketonuria in the population is about one in 25,000. For reasons to be explained later, this leads to the estimate that about one in every 50 individuals is a *Pp* heterozygote. Thus if II-9 marries, the risk that this will be a marriage between heterozygotes, that is, of type *Pp × Pp,* is one in 50, and since such matings result in one-fourth *pp* offspring, the risk for II-9 of having a phenylketonuric child is one in 200 ($\frac{1}{50} \times \frac{1}{4} = \frac{1}{200}$). She would be well advised to find out whether her prospective husband is the one of every 50 males who carries allele *p.*

The counselor could be even more specific in his advice if he knew the race of the fiancé of the young lady. For example, should the fiancé be an Englishman, his chances to be a carrier would be one in 80, and if he were a European Jew (an Ashkenazi), or a black, his chances to be a carrier would be very small indeed. This point will also be taken up in the discussion on "Behavioral Population Genetics," page 77.

DEAF-MUTISM: AN AUTOSOMAL RECESSIVE TRAIT

Pedigree analysis. Shown in Figure 9 is a pedigree of deaf-mutism in an Irish family. The pedigree has several interesting features. Autosomal recessive inheritance is suggested by the left side of the pedigree. Parents I-1 and I-2, and II-1 and II-2 have normal hearing, but several of their children are deaf. If we designate affected homozygotes by *dd* and normal carriers by *Dd,* we are tempted to hypothesize that I-1, I-2, II-1, and II-2 are *Dd* heterozygotes. Let us test this hypothesis by looking at the rest of the pedigree.

On the right side of the pedigree, in three successive generations, we see what often happens among the deaf. Affected individuals marry each other: *assortative mating* for this trait is common. Individuals I-3 and I-4 presumably are both *dd* homozygotes. They can have only *dd* offspring; and when II-11 marries II-10, their four children are deaf and, therefore, *dd* also.

Now we can test the hypothesis stated above. The deaf *dd* male III-9 marries the deaf female III-7. We would expect that all the children issuing from this marriage would be *dd* homozygotes, and, therefore, deaf. But as the pedigree shows, they are not. The six sons of III-7 and III-9 have normal hearing. This clearly suggests that, contrary to our earlier assumption, deafness in the branch of the family descending from I-1 is caused by genes at another chromosome locus than the deafness in the branch descending from II-1. If we hypothesize that both *dd* and *ee* homozygotes are deaf and genotypes *DD, Dd, EE,* and *Ee* have normal hearing, then female III-7 could be *DDee* and her husband III-9 could be *ddEE*. The two would be deaf, although for other reasons; and their children would all be *DdEe,* carriers of alleles *d* and *e,* but all normal.

This example illustrates *genetic heterogeneity,* an important genetic phenomenon. The phenotype of an individual is not always a reliable guide to his genotype. The same behavioral phenotype can have different genetic causes. Both branches of the family shown in Figure 9 are afflicted with deafness; in both branches inheritance is autosomal recessive, but genes at different loci are responsible for the condition in the two branches of the family. Often genetic heterogeneity of a condition is revealed only by a "breeding experiment," as was the case here. At present, we have no means of distinguishing between the many genetic causes of deafness; but we know that a variety of autosomal and sex-linked genes can cause the condition.

COLOR BLINDNESS: A SEX-LINKED TRAIT

Hereditary transmission of a trait from one generation to the next depends on the transmission of specific genes from parent to offspring. Genes are located on autosomes or sex chromosomes. If a gene is located on an X or Y chromosome, it is said to be sex-linked. Little is known about Y-linked inheritance. It appears that genes on the Y chromosome determine the course of prenatal sexual differentiation. If we possess a Y chromosome, we develop into a male; if we do not have a Y chromosome, we develop into a female (Money and Ehrhardt, 1972). As discussed previously, genes on the Y chromosome appear to have an influence on social behavior; but the information currently available is fragmentary and suggestive rather than conclusive. Much more is known about genes borne on the X chromosome (Box 5); and, therefore, the terms X-linked and sex-linked inheritance are often used synonymously. We will discuss only one X-linked trait: color blindness.

BOX 5

**SEX-LINKED RECESSIVE INHERITANCE
(X-LINKED INHERITANCE)**

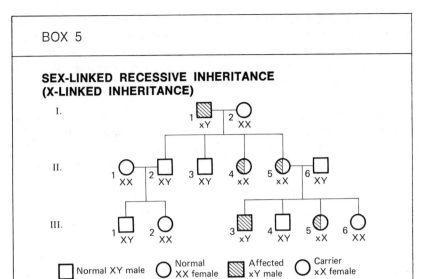

Prototype pedigree of X-linked recessive inheritance.

Shown is the typical pattern of transmission of a trait caused by a recessive gene carried on the X chromosome. Symbols *x* and *X* are used to designate the recessive and dominant allele of the X-linked gene. Illustrated are the following characteristics of X-linked recessive inheritance:

1. For all practical purposes, the recessive trait occurs only in males. Females are *xX* carriers of the recessive allele, but only rarely affected *xx* homozygotes.
2. The trait is never transmitted from father to son.
3. The recessive allele is passed from an affected male to all his daughters and none of his sons.
4. In a family, affected males are related to each other through carrier females.

Types of color blindness. Among the best known and most extensively studied X-linked behavioral traits are certain forms of color blindness. There exist many disorders of color vision, and most of them are heritable. But some are rare, others much more common. In rare instances, a person may be completely color blind; he may suffer from *achromatopsia*. He sees the world not in "living color" but in black, gray, and white. More common, but still rare, are individuals suffering from *tritanopia, a* form of partial color blindness in which blues and yellows are confused.

Quite common are four forms of red-green blindness; (a) *protanopia,* blindness for red; (b) *protanomaly,* low sensitivity for red;

(c) *deuteranopia,* blindness for green; and (d) *deuteranomaly,* low sensitivity for green. Without special examinations, the four forms are hard to distinguish. Roughly speaking, individuals afflicted by any one of these have difficulties when it comes to discriminating between red and green, hence the name red-green color blindness.

Sex differences. In different white populations the incidence of red-green blindness in males is from five to nine percent; in females it is much lower. Many females are carriers of color blindness alleles, but few are color blind. This sex difference is a direct consequence of the X-linked recessive nature of red-green blindness. Normal color vision is dominant over color blindness. Let us use the symbols X and x to designate X chromosomes bearing a dominant and a recessive allele. Since females have a pair of X chromosomes, there are three possible genotypes in females: XX, Xx, and xx. XX homozygotes and Xx heterozygous carriers have normal color vision; only xx recessive homozygotes are color blind. The situation is different in males. A male has only one X chromosome and is said to be *hemizygous* rather than homozygous or heterozygous. If a male carries an X-linked recessive allele $x,$ the recessive trait is expressed in him; he is color blind. Female xX are carriers, but male xY are affected.

Pedigree analysis. Many pedigrees of color blindness were published long before the X-linked mechanism of transmission of the trait was known. Part of two such pedigrees are reproduced in Figure 10, which should be compared with the figure in Box 5. Pedigree A is typical. In it we find the unmistakable pattern of X-linked recessive inheritance. Obviously, grandfather I-1, an xY male, transmits allele x to all of his daughters, who are xX carriers, and through them to some of his grandsons, who are xY and color blind. Generation II is "skipped"; only males in generation I and III are affected. Females transmit the trait, but are spared themselves.

Pedigree B appears to be atypical because generations are not skipped, male-to-male transmission appears to occur, and a color blind female is encountered in it. However, closer examination of the pedigree shows that, after all, it can be explained in terms of the principles of X-linked recessive inheritance. Consider first the apparent male-to-male transmission. Of course, the color blind male I-1 could not have transmitted an X-linked trait to his son II-2 since males transmit only Y chromosomes to their sons. Male II-2, an xY individual, must have received his allele x from his mother I-2. She must have been an xX carrier, and her mother (not shown in the pedigree) must have been either an xX heterozygote carrier or a color blind xx *homozygote.* That the mother carried allele x we know from

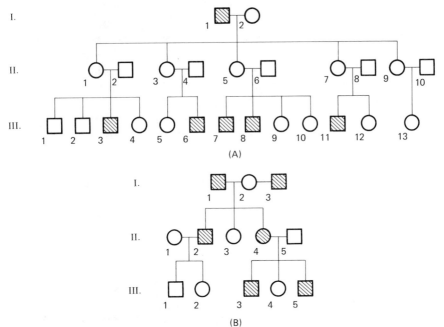

Figure 10. *Pedigrees of color blindness. Pedigree A is typical; B appears to be atypical. Both can be explained in terms of sex-linked recessive inheritance. [Adapted from* Principles of Human Heredity, *3d, by Curt Stern. W. H. Freeman and Company. Copyright © 1973. Reproduced by permission of W. H. Freeman and Company.]*

her son, male I-3, being color blind. Returning to female I-2, further evidence for her carrier status is found in the fact that she had a color blind daughter, II-4. And since a female can be color blind only if she received an allele *x* from both her parents, female I-2 must have been a carrier.

Let us look at one more interesting aspect of Pedigree B. Female II-4, having received alleles *x* from both her parents, is color blind. She marries a normal male, II-5. This, then, is a mating between an affected *xx* female and a normal *XY* male. In such cases, inheritance follows an interesting crisscross pattern: all sons are affected, like the mother; and all daughters are normal, like the father. The reason for this crisscross pattern is simple: in an *xx* by *XY* mating, all sons must be *xY* males; and all daughters must be *xX* females.

Theoretical models and scientific progress. The discussion of color blindness invites a general comment on scientific method. The pedigree reproduced in Figure 10B was first published in 1778, just one year after the first report about "persons who could not distinguish colours'' appeared in the *Philosophical Transactions* (see Stern, 1973, p. 305). We can imagine how confusing Pedigree B must have been to readers, particularly after several pedigrees of the type shown in Figure 10A had been published. The latter pedigree permitted the formulation of certain simple rules, such as those about ''affected grandfather, normal daughter, affected granson'' line of transmission. But all this must have appeared upset by Pedigree B. New assumptions had to be made; new empirical rules had to be formulated. Today, what once must have seemed to be contradictory findings can be deduced from a relatively simple model of the underlying mechanism, the Mendelian model.

C. C. Li, a well-known geneticist, points to another important lesson the phenomenon of color blindness teaches us about scientific method. According to Li (1971), environmental interpretations of sex differences in color blindness were widely and uncritically accepted not so long ago:

> How did the scientists before, say, 1900 explain the phenomenon? They did have explanations, very good ones, too. Males and females have different attitudes toward color in general. When buying a new car, a young man would ask about the things under the hood; a young woman would ask, what color is it? In the old days (not too long ago actually) girls used to sew and embroider with colorful threads. They have early contacts with color, upon which their beauty depends so much. The boys used to ride on horses, play ball, practice fencing, or engage in some other physical activities, none of which is related to color. The difference between boys and girls in their early contacts with color and the difference in value they attach to color exists and is real. Hence, there are more boys than girls who never learned to distinguish certain colors. This explanation, based on early environmental conditions, sounds perfectly reasonable and is even appealing in many respects except one—it is untrue.
>
> The case of color blindness brings out an extremely important general principle in scientific research; viz., the demonstration of the existence of an environmental difference does not automatically mean that it is the cause for the difference in the characteristics under study.

C. C. Li's warning that a perfectly reasonable and even appealing environmental explanation of a phenomenon does not guarantee its correctness applies to various mental abnormalities. For example, the theory that schizophrenia is caused by unhappy environmental circumstances during early childhood is widely accepted; but as we shall see next, there is more to the story.

SCHIZOPHRENIA

There is some question whether schizophrenia is caused by one or by many genes, and consequently, whether it should be discussed here or in the section on "Multifactorial Inheritance of Behavior," page 54. We decided, somewhat arbitrarily, to discuss it here and will provide a partial justification for our decision.

Behavioral symptoms. Schizophrenia is the most common of all mental diseases. About one in every 100 persons succumbs to it for longer or shorter periods. Almost 50 percent of the beds in our mental hospitals are occupied by schizophrenics. Among the primary symptoms of schizophrenia are disturbances of thinking; a dulling of emotions; and autism, a general withdrawal from the world. Among secondary symptoms are defects of attention, disturbances of voluntary activity, delusions, and hallucinations.

Thought processes of patients are often clearly abnormal. The patient forms peculiar and unusual associations and manifests "cognitive slipage" (Meehl, 1962). The strangeness of his thinking may not be obvious immediately and at all times, but ever so often we become aware of it. The emotions of patients are often dulled, and psychiatrists speak of "flattened," and "inappropriate affect." A patient may speak of a great personal loss, but not show the emotions we would expect to accompany his story. Or he may smile or giggle at inappropriate occasions. Events concerning him do not seem to touch him in the same way similar events affect others.

Many patients appear to withdraw for lengthy periods from contact with the world. They show no interest in their physical and social environment. They appear to live in a world of their own. They stop caring for themselves, become sloppy in attire, and seem unaware of the reaction of others to their unconventional behavior. They stop pursuing their regular work, they fail on their job, but they do not care. They can spend months and years sitting in a chair on a hospital ward, barely talking to anyone. Completely apathetic, they have lost their "will." In some instances, the disturbance of voluntary behavior may swing in the opposite direction. The patient may rush around excited and overactive, performing even the most senseless act with great investment of energy.

Best known to the layman, but not necessarily an accompaniment of every schizophrenic episode, are *hallucinations,* or false perceptions, and *delusions,* or false beliefs. The patient may hear voices that threaten him or command him to do things. He may be in "radio communication" with a committee of important persons that advises him and cares for him. And he may have visions of things not present. He may be deluded, often about his own person and the relation of others to him. He may believe to be God, the czar, or Napoleon; and he may feel spied upon and persecuted by people who wish to do him harm. He tenaciously holds on to his delusions and is not open to rational argument.

Schizophrenic episodes, presenting some although not necessarily all the symptoms mentioned, can last for days, weeks, or even years. Psychiatrists distinguish between *reactive* and *process* schizophrenia. In reactive schizophrenia the nervous breakdown occurs clearly in response to some stress, a death in the family, loss of a job or money, an unhappy love experience. In process schizophrenia, the onset of the disease is insidious, with disabling symptoms accumulating and becoming progressively worse until the breaking point is reached and hospitalization is required. Generally, the prognosis for recovery is better for reactive than for process schizophrenics.

Incidence in population and in relatives. The incidence of schizophrenia in the general population is about one in 100. We want to know whether the incidence of the disorder is larger among relatives of schizophrenics. If it were, we would have a reasonable, although not conclusive basis for the belief that schizophrenia is inherited. To establish the incidence of a disorder among relatives, we must start with a group of afflicted individuals. We call them the *index cases* or *probands* or *propositi* (singular, *propositus*) of our study. Next, we must find the relatives of each proband and determine their status. We establish how many of them are affected (*A*) and how many are normal (*N*). We can then compute the incidence (*I*) of the disorder by formula:

$$I = \frac{A}{A + N}$$

To illustrate, suppose we start with three schizophrenic probands and, on examining their children, find the following:

Proband 1: 2 normal, 1 schizophrenic child
Proband 2: 4 normal children
Proband 3: 3 normal children

The three probands have 9 normal and one schizophrenic child. Thus $I = 1/(9 + 1) = 1/10 = 10/100 = 10$ percent. If we wanted to generalize from such a small sample, we could conclude that the *empirical risk* a schizophrenic parent has to have schizophrenic children is 10 in 100. We speak of an empirical risk because it is inferred

TABLE 1.7 EMPIRICAL RISK OF SCHIZOPHRENIA
IN RELATIVES OF SCHIZOPHRENIC PROBANDS*

RELATIONSHIP TO PROBAND	TOTAL NUMBER OF RELATIVES	SCHIZOPHRENIC RELATIVES	PERCENTAGE RISK IN
1. Children of one schizophrenic parent	1227	170	13.9
2. Adopted children of schizophrenic mothers	47	5	10.6
3. Children of two schizophrenic parents	134	62	46.3
4. Sibs, neither parent schizophrenic	7535	731	9.7
5. Sibs, one parent schizophrenic	675	116	17.2
6. Siblings (lines 4 + 5)	8210	847	10.3
7. Monozygotic, identical twin	433	246	56.8
8. Monozygotic twin, reared apart	16	10	62.5
9. Dizygotic fraternal twin	644	74	11.5
10. Half sibs	311	11	3.5
11. Uncles, aunts	3376	123	3.6
12. Nephews, nieces	2315	61	2.6
13. Grandchildren	713	25	2.8

* The data in line 2 are from Heston (1970). All other entries are adapted from Slater and Cowie (1971).

or *induced* from actual observations and not *deduced* from theory. Empirical risks must be distinguished from theoretical risks, such as the one-in-four or 25 percent risk of affected children to issue from an Aa × Aa mating in the case of an autosomal recessive disorder (see Box 4). In what follows, we will discuss the empirical risk of schizophrenia in various relatives of schizophrenic probands.

Shown in Table 1.7 are data collected by European, American, and Japanese investigators over the last 50 years. The table reveals many interesting facts. The empirical risk of schizophrenia for individuals picked at random is 1 in 100. The table shows much higher risk figures for relatives of schizophrenics. In first-degree relatives, that is, children and siblings of patients, the risk is at least ten times as great (see entries in lines 1, 2, 6, and 9). In second-degree rela-

tives (see lines 10–13) the risk is only about three times the population risk, but it is still substantial.

Second-degree relatives share 25 percent, and first-degree relatives share 50 percent of their genes. The relatedness of identical,
one-egg or *monozygotic twins* is unique: they share 100 percent of
their genes. If relatives of schizophrenics are arranged according to
their increasing communality of genes, the corresponding risk figures
increase proportionately:

RELATEDNESS	ENTRY LINE	COMMON GENES IN PERCENT	RANGE OF RISK IN PERCENT
Second degree	10–13	25	2.6–3.6
First degree	1,2,6,9	50	10.3–13.9
Identical twins	7,8	100	56.8–62.5

Recent studies suggest that risk figures are also related to the
severity of the illness of the proband. For example, the risk of children of patients who never recovered or who were hospitalized for
many years is larger than the risk of children whose parent had only
a short bout with the disease. The relation betwen severity of disorder and risk is possibly reflected in the data on siblings. The overall risk for siblings is 10.3 percent (line 6). If we, however, divide
sibships as shown in lines 4 and 5, we find that there is more schizophrenia among siblings born to individuals who were hospitalized
than among siblings whose parents never required hospitalization.
And the risk of a child increases dramatically if both his parents were
hospitalized (see lines 1 and 3).

Twin studies. Twins play a particularly important role in the
study of human heredity. As is well known, there exist two types of
twins: *identical* and *fraternal.* Identical twins originate from a single
egg that was fertilized by a single sperm. The developing zygote, during an early mitotic division, separates into two independent em-
bryonic structures. Being derived from a single zygote, the two are
said to be *monozygotic;* and since both descend from the same
fertilized ovum, they are genetically identical. By contrast, non-
identical, *dizygotic* twins originate from two eggs—each fertilized by
a different sperm. Fertilization and development of the two just happens to occur simultaneously, that is, in the same and not in successive pregnancies. Thus in terms of their genes, two-egg, dizygotic
twins are not more alike than regular brothers or sisters; they are
fraternal twins.

Concordance. We call members of a pair of twins *concordant* if they agree and *discordant* if they disagree with respect to a characteristic. Since monozygotic (MZ) twins share 100 percent, and dizygotic (DZ) twins share only 50 percent of their genes, one would expect more concordance between MZ than between DZ twins.

Included in Table 1.7 are data on twins (lines 7, 8, 9). Let us note first that in the case of twins, risk values and concordance rates are the same. For example, shown in line 7 are 43 identical twins who had 246 affected co-twins. Of the 433 pairs, 246 were concordant for schizophrenia. Thus the concordance rate for schizophrenia was $246/433 = 0.5681 = 56.8$ percent, which is the risk value entered in the last column of line 7. With this in mind, let us look at the data. We find that MZ twins are more concordant than DZ twins. In fact, the difference, 56.8 versus 11.5, is striking, strongly implicating hereditary factors.

But environmentalists are not convinced; they see the other side of the coin. While the concordance of MZ twins is high, it is not 100 percent, as would be expected in view of their genetic identity. Thus schizophrenia must be caused by nongenetic, environmental factors. And as to the difference between MZ and DZ twins, environmentalists hold that this, too, has an environmental cause; the experiences of MZ twins tend to be more similar than those of DZ twins. A partial answer to these arguments is provided by Table 1.7. Fraternal twins, prenatally and postnatally, live in more similar environments than ordinary brothers and sisters. Yet as a comparison of lines 6 and 9 shows, in this case the greater environmental similarity does not seem to have an effect. Even more to the point is a comparison of lines 7 and 8. On record are 16 schizophrenic probands who were monozygotic twins, were separated shortly after birth from their twin sibling, and were reared in different families. Yet in ten of these 16 cases, the twins were concordant for schizophrenia. Thus the concordance rate in this group of MZ twins was 62.5 percent (see line 8). Although these twins were raised in different environments, they were even more concordant than the MZ twins raised in the same environment (see line 7). This precludes any simple environmental explanation of the high concordance of MZ twins.

Adoption and foster home studies. Monozygotic twins raised apart are ideal subjects for studies weighing the relative importance of environmental and genetic factors. But such twins are exceedingly rare and difficult to find. Easier to locate are adopted children of schizophrenic probands. It has often been argued that the high incidence of schizophrenia in children of patients was because of the "schizophrenic" environment in which the children were reared.

TABLE 1.8 PSYCHIATRIC DISORDERS IN FOSTER HOME-REARED CHILDREN OF SCHIZOPHRENIC MOTHERS*

	EXPERIMENTAL: MOTHER SCHIZOPHRENIC	CONTROL: MOTHER NORMAL	PROBABILITY
Number of subjects	47	50	
Number of males	30	33	
Age in years	35.8	36.3	
Schizophrenia	5	0	.024
Mental deficiency, IQ < 70	4	0	.052
Antisocial personalities	9	2	.017
Neurotic personality disorder	13	7	.052
More than 1 year in penal or psychiatric institution	11	2	.006
Felons	7	2	.054
Psychiatric discharge from army	8	1	.021

Source: Adapted from L. L. Heston, "The Genetics of Schizophrenic and Schizoid Disease," *Science,* January 1970, *167,* 249–256. Copyright 1970 by the American Association for the Advancement of Science.

* Considerable duplication of cases occurs in this table. For example, one mental defective was also schizophrenic; another had antisocial personality.

Many psychoanalysts implicated the schizophrenic mother of later patients, and the term "schizophrenogenic mother" has come into wide use. Heston (1966, 1970) examined the hypothesis that schizophrenia was caused by the genes schizophrenic mothers pass on to their children and not by the environment they provide for them. He studied the life histories of children born to schizophrenic mothers in an Oregon State Hospital. The children were separated from their mothers shortly after birth and brought up in orphanages and foster homes. Forty-seven such children formed the experimental group of Heston's study. Another 50 children, also separated from their mothers at an early age, were matched with the experimental subjects for sex, age, and type of foster home placement. These 50 children, born to normal mothers, formed Heston's control group. Some results of Heston's study are shown in Table 1.8 and in line 2 of Table 1.7. We see that 5 of the 47 children of schizophrenic mothers became schizophrenic, yielding a risk value of 10.6 percent. This is not appreciably lower than the 13.9 percent risk of children brought up by one schizophrenic parent (see line 1 of Table 1.7), raising questions about the notion of a schizophrenic home environment. The idea that the foster home and orphanage environment could have induced schizophrenia can be countered by the fact, shown in Table 1.8, that none of the 50 control subjects, who also were raised in foster homes, developed the disease.

Schizophrenic spectrum conditions. Heston's study became a landmark of psychiatric research because it suggested that the traditional definition of schizophrenia was too narrow: traditionally individuals were called schizophrenic only if they had been hospitalized for schizophrenia. But Heston's data (Table 1.8) show that among children of schizophrenic mothers there is not only an excess of schizophrenia, but also an excess of other psychiatric disorders. Antisocial behavior is common, particularly among males. To Heston, hospitalization is an artificial, unbiological criterion of disease since the "normal" relatives of schizophrenics, that is, those who never were hospitalized, frequently display schizophrenia-like or *schizoid* behavior. Many commit impulsive, unreasoning crimes such as arson, assault, poorly planned theft. Many are withdrawn individuals, heavy drinkers, sexual deviates. Female schizoids frequently react to ordinary social challenges with incapacitating attacks of panic and irrational fear. Others, both male and female, are eccentric, suspicious recluses. Like schizophrenics, schizoids are characterized by rigidity of thinking, flat emotions, an inability to enjoy life, touchiness and suspiciousness. Delusions and hallucinations may be rare, but some criminal, antisocial behavior of schizoids is bizarre enough to suggest "micropsychotic episodes." In short, Heston believes that it would be hard to find a sharp line of separation between schizophrenia and "schizoidia"; and he considers both to be manifestations of a common underlying genetic disorder. He is not alone with his views. Recently, the term "schizophrenic spectrum" conditions has come into use to refer to the whole gamut of behavioral disorders that stretch from the severe schizophrenic breakdowns requiring prolonged periods of hospitalization to the schizoid eccentricities of Heston's social recluses.

Mode of transmission. There can be no doubt any longer that schizophrenia is a hereditary disease. But its precise mode of transmission from parent to offspring has not yet been established (Slater & Cowie, 1971; Rosenthal, 1971). Many investigators believe that schizophrenia is a polygenic disorder, caused by many genes at different loci, each with a relatively small effect. Others believe that schizophrenia is caused by an autosomal recessive gene with a major effect. Still others hypothesize that the disease is caused by an autosomal dominant gene. All investigators agree that whatever the genes involved, environmental factors play a major role in their expression. Data like those reproduced in Table 1.7 need to be explained, and none of the hypotheses so far offered fits the data very well.

Consider, first, the recessive gene hypothesis (Box 4). If neither parent is schizophrenic and schizophrenia appears in the offspring, the mating must be of type $Aa \times Aa$. We would expect 25 percent schizophrenic children, but we find only 9.7 percent (Table 1.7, line 4). Or if both parents are schizophrenic (line 3, mating $aa \times aa$), we would expect 100 percent affected children; but we find only 46.3 percent.

Assuming next that schizophrenia is an autosomal dominant disorder (Box 3), we would expect 50 percent of the children of a patient to be affected; but only 13.9 percent are (line 1, mating $Aa \times aa$). If both parents were sick, we would expect 75 percent affected children; but we observe only 46.3 percent (line 3, mating $Aa \times Aa$). And of course, under any genetic hypothesis, concordance of monozygotic twins should be 100 percent, or close to it, but it is not (line 7).

According to Heston, past attempts to fit the data to a genetic model of transmission failed because of a narrow definition of schizophrenia that excluded schizoid individuals. When schizoids are included, as is done in Table 1.9, the picture changes considerably. Heston reanalyzed data from earlier studies in which information on schizoid relatives of schizophrenic probands was available and dealt with the genetic transmission of schizophrenic spectrum conditions rather than the transmission of schizophrenia per se. Heston's data are shown in Table 1.9. We see that the co-twins of schizophrenic MZ twins are just as likely to be schizophrenic as schizoid. Since MZ twins are genetically identical, this finding supports Heston's hypothesis that schizophrenic and schizoid disorders are alternative expressions of a single genotype. It then makes sense to lump the data for schizophrenics and schizoids together and to deal only with the values given in the last column of Table 1.9. If this is done, we see that 87.5 percent of the MZ co-twins of schizophrenic probands had a spectrum condition. This falls short of the theoretically expected 100 percent, but it approaches the value.

Let us look at the rest of Table 1.9. According to Heston, the data can be understood if we assume that all schizophrenic spectrum conditions are the expression of an autosomal dominant gene. Under this hypothesis, 50 percent of the children of one afflicted parent should be affected. The observed value was 49 percent (line 4, mating $Aa \times aa$). When both parents are sick (mating $Aa \times Aa$), 75 percent of the children should be affected; the observed value is 66.1 percent (line 5). Fifty percent of the parents and siblings of patients should have a spectrum condition disorder; the observed

TABLE 1.9 PERCENTAGE OF RELATIVES OF PROBANDS FOUND SCHIZOPHRENIC OR SCHIZOID

RELATIONSHIP TO PROBAND	TOTAL NUMBER OF RELATIVE	SCHIZO-PHRENIC PERCENT-AGE	SCHIZOIDS PERCENT-AGE	TOTAL SSC* PERCENT-AGE
1. Monozygotic twins	358	46.4	41.1	87.5
2. Parents	2741	9.2	34.8	44.0
3. Siblings	1191	14.3	31.5	45.8
4. Children of one schizophrenic parent	1000	16.4	32.6	49.0
5. Children of two schizophrenic parents	177	33.9	32.2	66.1
6. Grandchildren	882	4.3	22.8	27.1

Source: Adapted from L. L. Heston, "The Genetics of Schizophrenic and Schizoid Disease," *Science,* January 1970, *167,* 249–256. Copyright 1970 by the American Association for the Advancement of Science.
* SSC = Schizophrenic spectrum conditions.

values are 44.0 and 45.8 percent (line 2 and 3). Twenty-five percent of second-degree relatives such as grandchildren should be affected; and the observed value is 2.1 percent (line 6).

No one theory of transmission of schizophrenia is accepted by all students of the problem, and Heston's dominant gene theory is no exception. But the search for a plausible theory is deemed important and is carried on with vigor. Suppose Heston's theory were found to fit all data well, what would be the next step? A defective major gene implies overproduction or underproduction of an enzyme. It implies a biochemical error, an inability to carry out an essential metabolic step in a biochemical pathway. It implies a situation akin to the one we discussed in conjunction with phenylketonuria. The problem then reduces to a search for the biochemical defect that would have to be present in schizophrenics and their schizoid relatives. Once found, further progress could be made. Recent research suggests that the basic biochemical defect of schizophrenics concerns synthesis of neurotransmitters (Snyder, 1974). As in the case of PKU, an understanding of the nature of the defect may lead to means of detecting carriers of the defective gene long before the behavioral symptoms of the disease manifest themselves; and eventually, it may lead to a preventive treatment of schizophrenia.

MULTIFACTORIAL INHERITANCE OF BEHAVIOR

QUALITATIVE VERSUS QUANTITATIVE TRAITS

So far we have discussed traits which make it easy to categorize people. Individuals are Turner or Klinefelter patients; they have phenylketonuria or do not have it; they are color-blind or have normal color vision. Such traits, often called *qualitative traits,* permit us to pigeonhole people. They permit us to segregate them into classes or categories. In what follows we will discuss inheritance of quantitative traits, that is, traits which do not mark individuals as members of a class. Think of weight or body size. While it is possible to call some individuals skinny and others overweight, some small and others tall, we do realize that there are insensible gradations that lead from skinniness to overweight, from smallness to tallness. Differences between individuals are of degree rather than of kind, they are quantitative rather than qualitative, they cannot be used to pigeonhole individuals into neat categories. Differences between individuals must be measured on a continuous, quantitative scale, a scale without gaps. Traits measured on such a scale are usually called *quantitative traits.*

The best example of a behavioral quantitative trait is intelligence. There is no perceptible difference betwen an individual whose IQ is 101 and another whose IQ is 102. Transitions from one level of intelligence to another are smooth and continuous. The following discussion concentrates on inheritance of intelligence, but it can serve as introduction to the wider field of *quantitative genetics,* the study of inheritance of quantitative traits or phenotypes.

MONOGENIC VERSUS POLYGENIC OR MULTIFACTORIAL INHERITANCE

Geneticists believe that, in principle, inheritance of quantitative traits does not differ from inheritance of qualitative traits; both depend on transmission of genes from parent to offspring according to principles known from Mendelian genetics. But it is a curious fact of nature that qualitative differences between individuals are caused by one or a few genes with major effects, while quantitative differences tend to result from the joint action of many genes with individually small and hard to detect effects. Traits or phenotypes are the visible expression of underlying causes. Classified by cause, qualitative traits tend to be *monogenic,* while quantitative traits tend to be *polygenic.*

Let us note an additional important difference between monogenic and polygenic traits. Monogenic or major gene traits are relatively unaffected by environmental factors. The phenotype of an individual betrays his genotype in almost any environment. By contrast, polygenic traits are easily altered by environment. Environmental forces influence the expression of the minor genes making up "polygenic systems." Genic and environmental factors work together in shaping the phenotype of individuals, and it is impossible to say how much the phenotype of a given individual is due to his genotype and how much it is due to the environment in which he developed. To emphasize the fact that in the case of quantitative traits the phenotype expresses not only the action of genic, but also environmental factors, we will speak of *multifactorial traits* and multifactorial inheritance rather than of polygenic traits and polygenic inheritance; but the reader should remember that in current usage the two terms are synonymous.

INTELLIGENCE

Operational definition of intelligence. Intelligence is probably the most intensively studied quantitative behavioral trait. Psychologists define it operationally, that is, in terms of the procedure or "operation" used to measure it. The procedure involves the administration of a standardized intelligence test; thus operationally defined, a person's score on an intelligence test *is* his intelligence. Intelligence is what intelligence tests measure, and when psychologists talk about intelligence they are talking about a score (popularly known as IQ) on an intelligence test, for example, the Stanford-Binet test, or the Wechsler Adult Intelligence Scale, or the Army Alpha Test, and so on. And this is what we will speak about.

Stability and normal distribution of IQ scores. IQ scores have many remarkable properties, two of which, their stability and their distribution, shall be mentioned. (1) A person's IQ tends to remain almost the same over years. If on one occasion the measured IQ of individuals A, B, C was 80, 100, and 120, it is unlikely that, on another occasion, A will outscore B, or B will outscore C. The IQ of a person is a reliable, stable behavioral phenotype. (2) If a sample of many individuals is drawn at random from a population and the IQ of each individual is measured, one typically finds that only a few individuals have very low or very high IQs; most individuals have average or nearly average IQs. If we arrange all IQ scores in order of magnitude and plot them as shown in Figure 11, we obtain a "normal distribution," which graphically is characterized by a bell-shaped curve. IQ scores of a random sample of individuals tend to be normally distributed.

Multifactorial theory. Normal distributions of traits are common in biology. For example, if a sample of individuals is arranged according to size, few very small or very tall individuals are found;

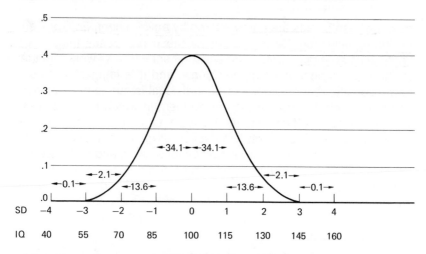

Figure 11. *Theoretical normal distribution of IQs. The standard deviation, SD, of IQ scores is 15 IQ points. About 34 percent of individuals have IQs between 100 and 115; 13.6 percent have IQs between 115 and 130, and so on, as shown in this figure. Except at extremes, below 70 and above 130, percentages shown are close to values observed in a white American population.*

most individuals are of average size. Body weight, body temperature, blood pressure, the age at which babies start to walk, girls start to menstruate, men become sexually mature, men and women die, and a host of other anatomical and physiological measures are distributed normally. Such distributions are explained by "multifactorial theory." Normal distributions are generated where a large number of independent factors, each having a small effect, cooperate in bringing about a trait. A numerical example shall make this clearer (see Table 1.10 in Box 6). Suppose four variables, *A, B, C,* and *D,* affect growth. Each variable is independent of every other, and each adds an inch to body size or subtracts an inch from it. Individuals receiving four plus factors are four inches taller than the average person, those receiving four minus factors are four inches smaller, and individuals receiving two plus and two minus factors are of average size. Of course, there are also those receiving three plus and one minus factor, and those receiving one plus and three minus factors: they are two inches above and two inches below average. The 16 possible combinations of the four plus and minus factors are shown in Table 1.10 and plotted in Figure 12 of Box 6. The reader will recognize that the graphed distribution resembles a normal distribution. Had we included many more independent factors with small positive and negative effects in our "multifactorial" model, the graph would resemble a bell-shaped curve even more closely.

Many psychologists subscribe to a multifactorial theory of in-

BOX 6

MULTIFACTORIAL MODEL AND VARIANCE

MULTIFACTORIAL MODEL

In the model shown in Table 1.10 accompanying this material, it is assumed that the phenotypes shown in the last column are caused by factors *A, B, C,* and *D.* (1) Each factor is a variable, since it can assume different values; in our model these values are represented by −1 and +1. (2) The factors act additively; each adds −1 or +1 to the phenotype. (3) The factors add small and approximately equal amounts to the phenotype. (4) Factors can substitute for each other. For example, an *A*(−1) can be balanced by a *B*(+1), or a *C*(+1), or a *D*(+1). (5) Factors are independent of each other: all possible combination of plus and minus factors are represented in the population (lines 1 to 16 of Table 1.10). Since each factor is represented by two alternative values (−1 and +1) and there are four factors, the total number of possible combinations is $2^4 = 16$.

TABLE 1.10 MODEL OF MULTIFACTORIAL GENERATION OF A NORMAL DISTRIBUTION

LINE	FACTORS				PHENO-TYPES (x)
	A	B	C	D	
1	+1	+1	+1	+1	+4
2	+1	+1	+1	−1	+2
3	+1	+1	−1	+1	+2
4	+1	+1	−1	−1	0
5	+1	−1	+1	+1	+2
6	+1	−1	+1	−1	0
7	+1	−1	−1	+1	0
8	+1	−1	−1	−1	−2
9	−1	+1	+1	+1	+2
10	−1	+1	+1	−1	0
11	−1	+1	−1	+1	0
12	−1	+1	−1	−1	−2
13	−1	−1	+1	+1	0
14	−1	−1	+1	−1	−2
15	−1	−1	−1	+1	−2
16	−1	−1	−1	−1	−4
SUM	0	0	0	0	0
SUMSQ	16	16	16	16	64
N	16	16	16	16	16
V = SUMSQ/N	1	1	1	1	4

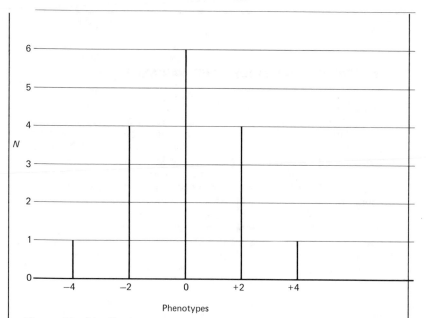

Figure 12. *Distribution of phenotypes produced by four independent, but additively acting factors. See Table 1.10.*

Figure 12 is a plot of the distribution of phenotypes shown in the last column of Table 1.10. The graphed distribution resembles a normal distribution (see Figure 11). Had we included many more independent factors with small positive and negative effects in our multifactorial model (see Table 1.10), the graph would resemble a bell-shaped curve even more.

VARIANCE

Variance is a statistical measure of variation. Factor scores (+1 and −1) in Table 1.10, and phenotypic scores (+4, +2, 0, −2, −4) vary. Variation could be indicated by the range of variation, for example, −1 to +1, or −4 to +4, but a conventional and highly useful measure of variation is variance. It is defined as the average of squared deviation scores of a distribution, a definition that will become clearer in a moment. Computation of variance is explained in most textbooks of statistics. The formula for variance has the general form:

$$V(X) = \frac{\Sigma(X - M)^2}{N} = \frac{\Sigma x^2}{N} \tag{1}$$

where X stands for a *raw score,* that is, some measure of a variable. IQ scores of 110, or 120, or 70 are examples of such raw scores. M stands for the *mean score* of a distribution. In the case of IQ scores, the mean score is usually taken to be 100. x represents a *deviation score,* that is, the deviation of a raw score from the mean of the population: $x = X - M$. For example, the deviation scores, x, for IQ scores 110, 120, and 70, are 10, 20, and −30.

In the table, all factor scores and phenotype scores can be taken to be deviation scores already. The sum of scores in each column is zero, so that the mean, M, is zero, too. Thus if we compute $x = X - M = X - 0$, nothing changes. Notice and remember that a distribution of deviation scores always adds up to zero.

In Table 1.10, to obtain the variance of each of the four factors and the variance of phenotypes

1. Square all deviation scores in each column
2. Get the sum of these squared deviation scores, SUMSQ
3. Get the average of squared deviation scores, that is, the variance, by dividing SUMSQ by N, the number of squared deviation scores in each column. SUMSQ/N = V.

You will have noted that these three steps execute the computations prescribed by formula 1 for variance given above, except that the deviation scores, x, need not be computed since all scores in the body of the table are already deviation scores. Note now two features of variance:

Additivity of Variances

The variance for each column of Table 1.10 is given in its bottom row. Observe and remember the remarkable fact that variances are additive. The phenotypic variance, $V(P)$, shown in the last column of the table, is the sum of factor variances: $V(A) + V(B) + V(C) + V(D) = V(P)$.

Independence of Variance from Mean of Population

Note and remember also that variance is independent of the mean of raw scores, M, since M is subtracted from every raw score, X, before variance is computed using deviation scores, x. Variance measures only variation around the mean of a distribution.

Variance and Standard Deviation

Textbooks of statistics discuss another measure of variation called standard deviation. This measure, often symbolized by SD or by the Greek letter sigma, σ. Standard deviation is the square root of variance:

$$SD = \sqrt{V} \qquad (2)$$

It obviously follows that $SD^2 = V$.

In Figure 11 we have shown the normal distribution of IQ scores in a white American population, a distribution characterized by an $M = 100$ and an $SD = 15$. The variance of IQs is $SD^2 = 15^2 = 225$. We shall see that one purpose of behavior-genetic analysis of IQ scores is to estimate what proportion of this variance ($V = 225$) is because of nature (heredity, genic factors) and how much of it is because of nurture (environment, prenatal and postnatal factors, nutrition, general health, home environment, education, life experiences of any kind).

telligence, but there is disagreement about the nature and mix of the factors that influence the performance of an individual on an intelligence test and thus his IQ score. In particular, there is controversy whether genetic or environmental factors predominate. Psychologists argue whether the observed distribution of IQ scores is mostly because of nature or nurture. Of course, just by looking at a distribution of IQ scores, we cannot tell what factors generated it. In our model (Box 6), variables A, B, C, and D could all represent environmental factors, or they could all represent genetic, heritable factors. Thus individuals could score high on an intelligence test (line 1 of Table 1.10) because they grew up well-fed and healthy, enjoyed an intellectually stimulating home environment, and had the very best of teachers; alternatively, they could score high because they inherited from their parents many "plus genes," genes that enhance their memory, speed up their thought processes, and strengthen their reasoning and problem-solving capabilities. Few psychologists today would defend an exclusively environmentalist or hereditarian position. Few would say that A, B, C, and D represent only environmental or only genetic factors. Rather, they would hold that the phenotypes of individuals, represented by the values in the last column of Table 1.10, are because of the additive effects of genetic factors, say A and B, and environmental factors, say C and D.

Heritability. The values in the last column of Table 1.10 (Box 6) represent phenotypic variation of a trait in a population. How can we evaluate what proportion of that variation is caused by genetic factors, and how much of it is because of environment? Geneticists have developed methods to give answers to these questions. The methods are too complex to be explained here but, using the values in Table 1.10, we will try to show what the methods accomplish. Shown in the last row of the table are $V(A)$, $V(B)$, $V(C)$, and $V(D)$, the variances for factors A, B, C, and D, and $V(P)$, the total phenotypic variance. As explained in Box 6, $V(A) + V(B) + V(C) + V(D) = V(P)$. Using numerical values, $1 + 1 + 1 + 1 = 4$. Suppose A, B, and C are genetic factors, and D is an environmental factor. Then genetic variance, $V(G)$ would equal $V(A) + V(B) + V(C) = 1 + 1 + 1 = 3$, and environmental variance, $V(E)$ would equal $V(D)$, that is, 1. Genetic and environmental variance can be expressed as proportions of total phenotypic variance. In our example, $V(G) / V(P) = \frac{3}{4}$, and $V(E) / V(P) = \frac{1}{4}$, and the two proportions add up to unity: $\frac{3}{4} + \frac{1}{4} = 0.75 + 0.25 = 1.0$. Geneticists have attached special symbols to these proportions:

$$V(G)/V(P) = h^2 \qquad (3)$$
$$V(E)/V(P) = e^2 \qquad (4)$$

The proportion h^2 is called heritability; it is the proportion of phenotypic variance caused by genetic factors. Similarly, e^2 is the proportion of phenotypic variance caused by environmental factors. Note
that

$$h^2 + e^2 = 1.0 \qquad\qquad (5)$$

If h^2 is large, e^2 is small and vice versa.

If in our multifactorial model (Box 6) variables A, B, C, and D
represented genetic factors, then $V(P)$ would be caused entirely by
genetic variance, $V(G)$ would equal $V(P)$, and h^2 would be 1.0. On the
other hand, if the four factors A, B, C, and D were environmental variables, $V(G)$ would not exist, h^2 would be zero, and e^2 would be 1.0
In actual data, h^2 is never 1.0 or 0.0. Phenotypic variation is never
caused entirely by genetic or environmental factors; nature and nurture are jointly responsible for observed variation.

Heritability is an important measure because among others, it
enables us to predict how closely children will resemble their parents. Suppose we select parents with an IQ of 120. As soon as a
child is born, the child is given up for adoption, and anyone in the
population can adopt it. With this as background, consider three
hypothetical cases:

1. *IQ is completely determined by genes, $h^2 = 1.0$ and $e^2 = 0$.*
In this case, the average IQ of the adopted children will be 120. Their
IQs will be the phenotypic manifestation of the genes they received
from their biological parents, whose IQ, as stated, was 120. The IQ
of the children will not be affected by the environment provided by
the adoptive parents.

2. *IQ is completely determined by environment, $h^2 = 0$ and
$e^2 = 1.0$.* In this case, the IQ of the children will resemble the IQ of
the adoptive parents. If children are given up for adoption randomly,
so that they grow up with parents of different IQ, their average IQ will
be 100, which is the mean IQ of the population and presumably also
the mean IQ of the adoptive parents. The IQ of the children will not
reflect the IQ of their biological parents.

3. *IQ is determined equally by heredity and environment, $h^2 =
0.50$ and $e^2 = 0.50$.* In this case, the genes received from the parents
will tend to raise the IQ of the children to 120, while the environment
provided by the adoptive parents (a random sample from the population) will tend to lower the IQ to the population mean of 100. In effect,
the average IQ of the children will fall midway between 100 and 120;
it will be 110.

Regression to the mean. Note that the children "regress"
toward the mean of the population. When $h^2 = 0$ and $e^2 = 1.0$, re-

gression is complete; the IQ of the children regresses from the parental mean to the population mean. When $h^2 = 1.0$ and $e^2 = 0$ there is no regression.

This analysis suggests one use of h^2. Heritability of IQ in the white American population is about 0.80. Suppose we wished to predict the average IQ of children of parents whose IQ is 120. The method is simple:

1. Compute the deviation, x, of the parental mean score, the so-called midparent, MP, from the population mean: $x = MP - M = 120 - 100 = 20$.
2. Multiply x by h^2: $x \times h^2 = 20 \times 0.80 = 16$.
3. Add the result of step 2 to the population mean: $M + 16 = 100 + 16 = 116$. The predicted IQ of the children is given by step 3; it is 116. Note again the regression toward the population mean. However, with $h^2 = 0.80$, regression is less pronounced than with $h^2 = 0.50$.

To check whether you know how to use h^2, compute the predicted IQ of children of parents whose mean IQ, $MP = 70$. Your answer should be 76. Here, too, the IQ of children regresses to the mean of the population. In this case, however, the children are not less but more intelligent than their parents. Do one more computation: compute the average IQ of children of parents whose IQ is 100.

Estimating heritability from regression to mean. How do we establish the heritability of a trait? We have not discussed this question yet, but one method suggests itself: the phenomenon of "regression to the mean" can be used. Suppose you obtained scores on many, randomly chosen parents and their children. If the mean score of the children regressed halfway to the mean of the population, $h^2 = 0.5$ and e^2 is 0.5. If it regressed all the way to the mean, $h^2 = 0$, and $e^2 = 1.0$. There are, however, problems with this method. Heritability is supposed to measure only the contribution of genetic factors to similarity between parents and children. But if parents bring up their children they not only pass on their genes to them, but also shape their behavior by shaping their environment. Genetic and environmental factors are hopelessly confounded. To make the method work, we must rely on cases where children were separated from their parents early in life. We encountered this problem already in the section on schizophrenia. In what follows, we will discuss related but somewhat different methods.

MZ twins raised apart. The best estimates of heritability of intelligence come from studies of identical twins who were separated early in life and raised in different environments. Data for 69 pairs of such twins are shown in Table 1.11 The data were collected by

TABLE 1.11 IQs FOR
MZ TWINS REARED APART

SHIELDS		NEWMAN ET AL.		JUEL-NIELSEN	
A	B	A	B	A	B
63	73	77	92	99	108
69	71	78	66	99	105
71	75	79	88	100	94
74	69	84	85	100	94
76	79	85	97	104	99
79	84	88	90	104	103
83	89	89	93	105	97
84	68	90	91	111	116
85	84	94	102	112	100
86	84	94	95	114	124
86	85	96	77	114	113
88	110	99	101	120	128
89	93	102	96		
89	84	105	106		
90	107	105	115		
91	84	106	89		
93	76	109	116		
94	76	116	92		
95	87	122	127		
95	79				
95	101				
96	100				
96	99				
96	97				
98	110				
98	94				
99	108				
99	97				
101	87				
102	108				
103	116				
105	105				
107	105				
107	111				
107	106				
109	102				
113	111				
121	121				

N	$= 38$	N	$= 19$	N	$= 12$
$Mean$	$= 93.0$	$Mean$	$= 95.7$	$Mean$	$= 106.8$
SD	$= 13.5$	SD	$= 13.2$	SD	$= 9.3$
$Diff$	$= 6.2$	$Diff$	$= 8.2$	$Diff$	$= 6.4$

Source: Adapted from A. R. Jensen, "IQs of Identical Twins Reared Apart," Behavior Genetics, 1970, 1, 133–148. Used by permission of Plenum Publishing Corporation.

Shields (1962) in England, Newman, Freeman, and Holzinger (1937) in the USA; and Juel-Nielsen (1965) in Denmark. Jensen (1970) used them in an important theoretical paper, and we abstracted them from a table prepared by him. We will use the data to compute "MZ difference scores" and MZ correlations.

Difference scores. Having the IQs for both members of each twin pair, we can compute the absolute difference between their IQs. The mean differences $M(d_{MZ})$, between A and B twins in the three studies were:

Shields	6.2
Newman	8.2
Juel-Nielsen	6.4

Are these differences large or are they small? What standard of comparison can we use? One standard is provided by the average difference in scores obtained by one and the same individual on two matched forms of an IQ test. In one often cited study (Terman and Merrill, 1937) that difference was 4.68 IQ points. We compared the scores not of one but of two persons; yet the difference was only one third larger. Of course, and this is the point we wish to make, we did not compare the scores of any two individuals, but the scores of a pair of genetically identical individuals.

What happens if we compare the scores of genetically different, unrelated individuals? Such comparison provides a second standard against which to judge the difference scores of monozygotic twins. Suppose we picked at random two individuals from a population. The maximum possible difference in their IQs will be determined by the range of IQs encountered in that population. If IQs ranged from 55 to 145, the maximum possible difference score would be 90. If the range of scores were more restricted, the maximum possible difference score would be correspondingly smaller. It should also be intuitively clear that if we randomly picked many pairs of individuals, the distribution of difference scores would be related to the shape of the distribution of IQs in the population. If only few individuals had very low or very high IQs, we would only rarely match up individuals with maximally different IQs. Small difference scores would be common, large differences would be rare. What we have tried to say in many words, mathematical statisticians have captured in a single formula (Jensen, 1970). It relates the mean absolute difference score, $M(d_p)$, of all possible pairs to the standard deviation, SD, of IQs in the sampled population:

$$M(d_p) = (2SD)/\sqrt{\pi} = 1.13SD \tag{6}$$

For example, the standard deviation of IQ scores in the United States is about 15. Therefore, the expected mean absolute IQ difference between pairs of individuals picked at random, $M(d_p) = 1.13 \times 15$, or approximately 17 IQ points.

We can apply this formula to compute $M(d_p)$ in the populations sampled by Shields, Newman, and Juel-Nielsen. The standard deviations of IQ scores in the three populations, estimated from the scores of A and B twins, the corresponding mean IQ differences of randomly picked individuals, and the observed mean differences (shown in Table 1.11) were

	SD	$M(d_p)$	$M(d_{MZ})$
Shields	13.5	15.2	6.2
Newman	13.2	14.9	8.2
Juel-Nielsen	9.3	10.5	6.4

Clearly, the IQs of monozygotic twins, even though the twins were separated early in life, are more similar than the IQs of randomly paired individuals. $M(d_{MZ})$ is strikingly smaller than $M(d_p)$. If in this country, to win a bet, you were to name, without the benefit of testing, two individuals whose IQs differed by no more than 17 points, odds would be heavily stacked in your favor if you named monozygotic twins. You would lose your bet half of the time if you named two individuals chosen at random.

We are now ready to discuss one way in which MZ twins reared apart help us to estimate the heritability of intelligence. We remember from previous pages that the phenotypic variance, $V(P)$, of quantitative traits is composed of genotypic variance, $V(G)$, and environmental variance, $V(E)$:

$$V(G) + V(E) = V(P) \tag{7}$$

If we divide both sides of this equation by $V(P)$, we obtain

$$\frac{V(G)}{V(P)} + \frac{V(E)}{V(P)} = 1.0 \tag{8}$$

and we recall that, by definition, $V(G)/V(P) = h^2$ and $V(E)/V(P) = e^2$, so that,

$$h^2 + e^2 = 1.0$$

Monozygotic twins are genetically identical. If they differ behaviorally, the difference must be because of environmental, nongenetic causes. On the other hand, if unrelated individuals differ behaviorally, this must be because of environmental *and* genetic causes. Without going into mathematical details, it can be appreciated that $M(d_{MZ})$, the average difference in IQ of monozygotic twins reared apart, is related to $V(E)$, and that the mean difference in IQ of randomly paired individuals, $M(d_p)$, is related to $V(G) + V(E)$, that is $V(P)$. Thus the ratio of $M(d_{MZ})/M(d_p)$ is related to $V(E)/V(P)$, that is, e^2. More precisely,

$$[M(d_{MZ})/M(d_p)]^2 = e^2 \qquad (9)$$

Let us then use formula 8 and our twin data to estimate e^2 of IQ. We will compute two sets of values by setting $M(d_p)$ equal to 17, which is based on an SD of 15, the U.S. population value; and by setting $M(d_p)$ equal to the values based on the standard deviations of the three separate studies:

	$M(d_{MZ})$	$M(d_p)$	e^2	$M(d_p)$	e^2
Shields	6.8	17	0.16	15.2	0.20
Newman	8.2	17	0.23	14.9	0.30
Juel-Nielsen	6.4	17	0.14	10.5	0.37
Average e^2:			0.18		0.29

From the relationship $h^2 + e^2 = 1$, it follows that $h^2 = 1 - e^2$. Above we obtained two average values of e^2, namely, 0.18 and 0.29. Using 0.24, the mean of the two, we estimate the heritability of IQ, h^2 to be $1 - 0.24$, that is 0.76.

MZ correlations. We have used the difference between the IQs of monozygotic twins reared apart to estimate the heritability of intelligence. We will now use the correlation between their IQs to obtain another estimate of h^2. The correlations for the three studies were

Shields	.78
Newman	.67
Juel-Nielsen	.69

These are "double entry" correlations, with each twin pair entering computations twice, once in the order shown in Table 1.11 and once in reverse order, for example, $A = 95$ and $B = 87$, plus $A = 87$ and $B = 95$. The average of the three correlations is .71, which after we apply to it a so-called "correction for attenuation," becomes .75. This correlation, $r = .75$, is another estimate of h^2, the heritability of intelligence, as we shall try to show next. Figure 13 will help explain the reasoning behind this conclusion. Figure 13 is a "scatter diagram" of the correlation ($r = .78$) obtained by Shields. The graph is symmetrical about the left-to-right, 45° diagonal because the principle of double entry was also used in preparing it: each pair of twins

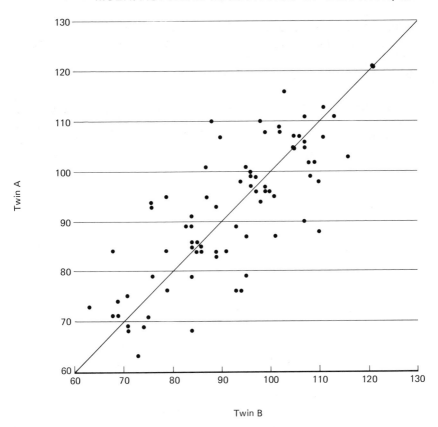

Figure 13. *Correlation of Shields Data.*

is represented by two points. How do we interpret what we see? MZ twins are genetically identical. If only genes were responsible for an individual's behavior, the two members of a twin pair would have identical scores; and all points representing twin pairs would fall on the left-to-right diagonal of Figure 13. In this case the correlation *r* would be 1.0. In fact, the scatter diagram shows that the scores of *A* twins often differed from the scores of *B* twins, but not by much: all plotted points fall close to the diagonal. A wide scatter of points about the diagonal then indicates large differences between twins and a small correlation, *r*, between them, and vice versa; a narrow scatter indicates small differences between them and a large *r*.

The study of these correlations is important because differences between MZ twins must be entirely because of environment. In the case of monozygotic twins the scatter of points about the diagonal is a direct expression of environmental variance, $V(E)$. The larger the scatter, the larger $V(E)$ is. If scatter is absent, that is, if all points representing twin pairs "vanish" into the diagonal, $V(E) = 0$. Recall now that, according to equation 7, $V(G) + V(E) = V(P)$. Thus if $V(E) = 0$, phenotypic variance, $V(P)$, equals genotypic variance, $V(G)$, and h^2 which by definition is $V(G)/V(P)$, equals 1.0. But note that when scatter is absent, r also equals 1.0, which establishes that, in the case of MZ twins, the correlation between them estimates heritability, h^2. Returning to the three IQ studies, we recall that the average corrected correlation in IQ between MZ twins was 0.75, suggesting that in the English, American, and Danish white populations sampled by Shields, Newman, and Juel-Nielsen, 75 percent of the phenotypic variance of IQ scores is because of heredity, while under present conditions only 25 percent of the variance is because of environmental causes. These values are close to those we arrived at when we based our estimates on observed differences between MZ twins.

Unrelated persons reared together. We discussed how genetically identical individuals, MZ twins, raised in different environments help us estimate the heritability of IQ. We will now see how genetically different individuals reared in the same environment can be used for the same purpose. We can, for example, compute correlations between adoptive parents and their adopted children, or we can compute correlations between unrelated adopted children reared by their adoptive parents in a common family environment. Several studies doing just that have been published (Jensen, 1969); and although observed IQ correlations differ from study to study, the correlations are rarely higher than .35 and rarely lower than .15. The interpretation of these correlations mirrors, that is, reverses the interpretations of MZ twin correlations. One correlation involving MZ IQ scores was shown in Figure 13. We do not present an analogous scatter diagram for unrelated individuals, but the reader can imagine how it would look. If common environment caused IQ of unrelated individuals to become identical, all points representing pairs of such individuals would fall on the left-to-right diagonal, and r would be 1.0. This correlation would tell us that whatever genetic differences existed between the members of each pair did not matter. The genotype of individuals did not affect their phenotype. Whatever phenotypic variation existed in the population was environmental variation; genotypic variation, $V(G)$, was overriden by environmental forces; phenotypic variation, $V(P)$, equaled environmental variation, $V(E)$; e^2, which by definition is $V(E)/V(P)$ was 1.0; and h^2 (which is $1 - e^2$) was 0. On the other hand, if the points representing pairs of individuals reared in the same environment were scattered widely, if there were no apparent order to their scatter, if the IQ of one member of a pair did not tell us anything about the IQ of the other, if, in brief, the correlation between individuals were 0, we would infer that environment did not contribute systematically to phenotypic variation, that e^2 was

0 and h^2 was 1.0. This juxtaposition of the two extreme possibilities leads to the conclusion that the correlation *r* of unrelated individuals reared in the same environment estimates e^2, the same way the correlation of related individuals reared in different environments estimates h^2. The two types of studies complement each other.

Correlation for IQ and genetic relatedness. So far we reported two extreme sets of studies. The studies were extreme in the sense that they dealt with unrelated individuals who have no genes in common and MZ twins who share all their genes. But, of course, many degrees of relatedness exist between these two extremes. Thus parent and child share 50 percent of their genes, and so do siblings; grandparent and grandchild share 25 percent of their genes, and so do uncle and nephew, or aunt and niece. First cousins share ⅛, and second cousins $\frac{1}{16}$ of their genes. A prediction deduced from polygenic theory and the theory of correlation is that phenotypic correlations between individuals will, on the average, correspond to the proportion of genes these individuals share. Thus, disregarding all environmental factors, the predicted correlation between parent and child is .50, between grandparent and grandchild it is .25, and so on.

In 1963, Erlenmeyer-Kimling and Jarvik reviewed 52 studies of correlations of IQ scores among related and unrelated persons. Jensen added various kinship correlations not included in Erlenmeyer-Kimling's and Jarvik's review and published his and their data in a table that is partly reproduced in our Table 1.12. We note a remarkable and impressive correspondence between correlations predicted from genetic theory and observed correlations. But there are departures from prediction, particularly where individuals of the same degree of relatedness had been reared in the same or different environments. As we have already seen, such departures are valuable to us. They show that a purely genetic theory cannot account for the data. Environment enters the picture and affects IQ. At the same time, the departures from purely genetic prediction are relatively small, showing that, under present conditions of child rearing, environment has a lesser effect on IQ than heredity. How much smaller is the effect of environment? This is what the relative sizes of e^2 and h^2 tell us. On earlier pages and in what follows, we assume h^2 of IQ to be 0.80, although many researchers consider this value too high, others too low. Empirical studies of heritability are fraught by innumerable difficulties of a methodological and theoretical nature, none of which we have mentioned here. The "true" value of h^2 changes with environmental and genetic circumstances. It differs from population to population, and it changes in time as the populations and environments change. Yet evidence from a variety of studies suggests that h^2 of IQ is almost certainly larger than 0.50. The view, held by some (Kamin,

TABLE 1.12 CORRELATIONS FOR INTELLECTUAL
ABILITY: OBTAINED AND THEORETICAL VALUES

CORRELATION BETWEEN	NO. OF STUDIES	OBTAINED MEDIAN	THEO-RETICAL VALUE
Unrelated persons			
Children reared apart	4	−.01	.00
Foster parent and child	3	+.20	.00
Children reared together	5	+.24	.00
Collaterals			
Second cousins	1	+.16	+.063
First cousins	3	+.26	+.125
Uncle (or aunt) and nephew (or niece)	1	+.34	+.25
Siblings, reared apart	3	+.47	+.50
Siblings, reared together	36	+.55	+.50
Dizygotic twins, different sex	9	+.49	+.50
Dizygotic twins, same sex	11	+.56	+.50
Monozygotic twins, reared apart	4	+.75	+1.00
Monozygotic twins, reared together	14	+.87	+1.00
Direct line			
Grandparents and grandchild	3	+.27	+.25
Parent (as adult) and child	13	+.50	+.50
Parent (as child) and child	1	+.56	+.50

Source: Adapted from Jensen, "How Much Can We Boost IQ and Scholastic Achievement?" *Harvard Educational Review,* 1969, *39* (1), 1–123.

1974), that intelligence is solely a product of environmental circumstances unaffected by heredity appears untenable.

Equality of environmental opportunity and IQ. Jensen (1969 a, b) has represented the relationship between e^2 and h^2 in a graphic form. He asked two questions: (1) How would the distribution of IQ scores look if, by some feat of magic, we could eliminate all genetic differences between individuals and everyone had an equal number of plus and minus genes for intelligence, leading to an average IQ of 100? And (2) how would the distribution look if genetic differences remained as they are now but everyone were exposed to the same physical, educational and cultural environment?

The answers to these two questions are represented in Figure 14*A* and *B* taken from Jensen (1969 a, b). According to current esti-

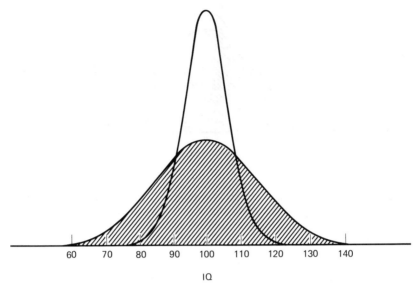

Figure 14A. *Comparison of what the distribution of IQs theoretically would be if all genotypes were identical (for IQ 100) in an "average" environment (assuming a normal distribution of environmental advantages) and all variance were only because of non-genetic (environmental) factors (heavy line). Under these conditions the heritability (H) of IQs would be zero, instead of .80 as in the present population. The shaded curve represents the normal distribution of IQs in the present population. [From A. R. Jensen, "Reducing the Heredity-Environment Uncertainty," in* Environment, Heredity, and Intelligence, *Reprint Series No. 2, 1969, 209–243. Copyright © 1969 by the President and Fellows of Harvard College. Reprinted by permission.]*

mates, the average IQ of the white American population is 100, and the standard deviation, *SD,* of IQ scores is 15 (see Figure 11). Variance, *V* is *SD²*. Therefore, the total phenotypic variance, *V(P)*, of IQ scores is 15² or 225. We must now partition *V(P)* into its two components, *V(G)* and *V(E)*. We use *h²* and *e²* for this purpose:

$V(G)$ = Variance because of heredity   : $V(P) \times h^2 = 225 \times 0.80 = 180$
$V(E)$ = Variance because of environment : $V(P) \times e^2 = 225 \times 0.20 = 45$
$V(P)$ = Phenotypic variance   : $V(P) = V(G) + V(E) = 180 + 45 = 225$

Now we compute the standard deviation of *V(G)* and *V(E)*:

$SD(G) = \sqrt{V(G)} = \sqrt{180} = 13.42$
$SD(E) = \sqrt{V(E)} = \sqrt{45} = 6.71$
$SD(P) = \sqrt{V(P)} = \sqrt{225} = 15.00$

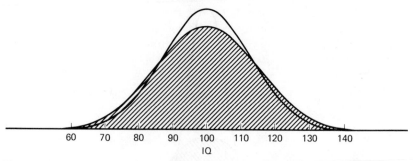

Figure 14B. *The theoretical distribution of IQs if all variance resulting from environmental factors were eliminated (with everyone having an "average" environment) and all the remaining variance were due only to genetic factors (heavy line). Under these conditions the heritability (H) of IQs would be 1.00. The shaded curve represents the normal distribution of IQs in the present population, in which H = 0.80. [From Jensen, 1969.]*

The standard deviation, as explained in most introductory textbooks of statistics, permits one to estimate the range of scores of a distribution above and below the mean of a population. For all practical purposes, one hundred percent of all scores fall in the range of $\pm 3\ SD$ around the mean. In the case of IQ scores, then mean is 100:

DISTRIBUTION BECAUSE OF	SD	MEAN − 3 SD	MEAN	MEAN + 3 SD
Heredity (G)	13.42	59.7	100	140.3
Environment (E)	6.71	79.8	100	120.2
G + E	15.00	55.0	100	145.0

These are the values Jensen used to graph the distributions shown in Figure 14. The figure shows a truly remarkable prediction of behavior-genetic research. Creating an environment that would be equal for all and favor none, would not change matters much. (Figure 14B), But creating a genetically uniform man, with everyone his neighbor's genetic equal, would indeed contribute to a pronounced reduction of individual differences in intelligence (Figure 14A). There would be fewer Einsteins and Merit Scholarship winners but there would also be fewer mentally retarded.

BEHAVIORAL POPULATION GENETICS

Until now, we dealt almost exclusively with family genetics of behavior. We studied similarities between members of a family and differences between families. Here we will deal with *population genetics.* Instead of asking whether such traits as phenylketonuria, color blindness, or high intelligence occur frequently in certain families, we will ask whether they are common in some and rare in other populations. Today, as is well known, the question of hereditary differences between populations is the subject of heated and sometimes acrimonious debates. Most hotly debated is the issue of IQ differences between populations, and we will deal with this subject later. First, however, we will introduce several concepts of population genetics and give selected examples of population genetic research.

SOME CONCEPTS OF POPULATION GENETICS

Mendelian populations. Until fairly recently, human beings lived in relatively small groups, and this is true in many parts of the world even today. There is much interbreeding within such groups and little intermarrying between them. Think of a small remote mountain village. Everyone is a fourth, or third, or second cousin of everyone else. Individuals in the village share many of their genes. Only rarely are new genes "imported" into the community by strangers settling down in the village; only rarely are genes lost to the community by emigration of individuals who possess some genes no one else in the village possesses. Biologists use the term *Mendelian population* to refer to such "reproductive communities of individuals who share in a common gene pool" (Dobzhansky, 1955).

In theory, all members of a species can interbreed. They form one large reproductive community, one large Mendelian population. Actually, however, mostly because of geographic barriers to free interbreeding, species tend to split into subspecific Mendelian populations, *subspecies* or *races.* These, in turn, are often composed of numerous local breeding communities or *demes.*

Within most species the flow of genes is hampered primarily by geographic barriers, often simply the distance separating racial groups or demes. Yet within a species there is always some gene diffusion. "Although flies native to California do not usually mate with flies from Texas, the genes of the California population may percolate, although slowly, through a chain of geographically intermediate populations, to Texas, or anywhere else in the species area." (Dobzhansky, 1958, p. 27) Demes and races are genetically open systems; species are not. Species are genetically closed Mendelian populations. They do not share in a common gene pool with other species.

Within the human species the flow of genes between groups of individuals is hampered not only by distance, but also by culture, custom, and prejudice. Most racial groups do not interbreed freely, remaining relatively genetically isolated, even if inhabiting the same geographic area. Ethnic and religious groups do not intermarry readily, even if living in adjacent quarters of a city. And in many class-conscious societies, little interbreeding occurs between members of different social classes. Because of such mating patterns, mankind is subdivided into innumerable Mendelian populations, populations kept in relative genetic isolation by geography, race, ethnicity, religion, and social class. Behavioral population genetics studies behavioral differences between members of such Mendelian populations.

Gene pools. The totality of genes possessed by mankind constitutes its gene pool. Since mankind is subdivided into numerous Mendelian populations, its gene pool is subdivided also. The content of the many gene pools can differ. To illustrate, the gene pools of populations of Central Africa contains genes for skin pigmentation, which the gene pools of North European populations do not harbor. And the gene pools of African pygmy populations must contain different genes for body growth than the gene pools of the tall Watusi tribes. These examples show that gene pools of different populations often hold different sets of genes for morphological traits. Behavioral population genetics asks whether they also contain different sets of genes affecting behavior. For example, do the gene pools of some races contain more "plus genes" for intelligence than the gene pools of other races? Such specific questions lead to more general questions which we must take up next.

Natural selection. Presumably, each of the many gene pools of mankind contains a different set of genes. Natural selection is the principal force causing the differences. Suppose that southern colonists settle a northern region. At first the southern ancestral population and its northern colony will have similar gene pools; but in time, the pools will come to differ. Assume that in the two populations there exist allelic genes C and c. Assume also that homozygotes CC and heterozygotes Cc are better equipped to withstand cold weather and the rigors of the north than homozygotes cc. In the mild southern climate, the genotype of an individual did not matter. All three genotypes survived and reproduced well; none had a *selective advantage* over the others. In the northern climate, however, genotype cc is at a definite reproductive disadvantage. It readily contracts tuberculosis and other respiratory diseases and often succumbs before reproducing. In the inclement northern climate genotypes CC and Cc are *reproductively fitter* than genotype cc; that is, they contribute more offspring to succeeding generations. The effect on the gene pool of the northern population is predictable: the proportion of fitness-enhancing alleles C will increase in the northern gene pool, while the proportion of fitness-reducing alleles c will decrease. If, for example, in the southern gene pool the proportions of alleles C and c were ¼ and ¾, with the passage of time the proportions of the two alleles in the northern gene pool will change to ½ and ½, ¾ and ¼, $\frac{9}{10}$ and $\frac{1}{10}$, and so on. Thus natural selection will bring about a difference between the northern and southern gene pools.

Environmental circumstances determine the selective value of genotypes. In one environment, a given genotype may be selectively neutral. In another environment, the same genotype may be at a selective advantage or disadvantage. In the South, genotype cc is selectively neutral; it neither enhances nor reduces reproductive fitness. In the North, the same genotype is at a selective disadvantage relative to CC and Cc. While, strictly speaking, genotypes—rather than genes—are selected for or against, geneticists often speak of the selective fitness-enhancing or fitness-reducing value of genes. Thus in the north, allele C has a positive and allele c a negative value; in the south, both alleles are neutral with regard to fitness.

In conclusion, note carefully the essence of natural selection. Whether an individual is "selected" to contribute his genes to the gene pool is determined by his genotype and the particular environment in which he finds himself. If he carries genes which, in a specific environment, enhance his chances to reproduce, he "survives genetically"; that is, he transmits his genes to the next generation. If some of his genes interfere with reproduction, he may suffer "genetic death"; his genes may not be passed on. In the modern definition of natural selection, "survival of the fittest" means "genetic survival of the reproductively fittest." Fitness, without exception, refers to reproductive fitness only. From an evolutionary point of view, a man with ten children is ten times fitter than a man with one child.

Phenotypic, genotypic, and genic frequencies. Geneticists characterize a Mendelian population by listing the proportions of different alleles contained in its gene pool. We used this method in our example of a southern and a northern population. We characterized the two populations by saying that the gene pool of one contained ¼ alleles C and ¾ alleles c, while the gene pool of the other contained $\frac{9}{10}$ C and $\frac{1}{10}$ c alleles. How do geneticists arrive at such estimates?

The reader realizes that nobody ever observes genes, such as C or c; or genotypes, such as CC or cc gene pairs. But phenotypes are observable, such as individuals displaying the symptoms of phenylketonuria, Huntington's chorea, color blindness, or schizophrenia. We must thus arrive at estimates of gene frequencies from observations of phenotypic frequencies. We shall explain how this is done by using an analogy. Suppose every morning on your way to work you meet a blind person and you note that he wears black or white socks. On many days, however, he wears one white and one black sock. Being statistically minded, you tabulate your observations with the following results:

black–black	1 in 16 days
white–black	3 in 16 days
black–white	3 in 16 days
white–white	9 in 16 days

You assume that the man has many black and white socks in a drawer and that because of his blindness he daily pulls two socks out randomly. Sometimes the colors match and sometimes they do not. Can you infer from your tabulation what the proportions of white and black socks in the drawer are? The answer is that in the drawer the proportion p of white socks is ¾, and the proportion q of black socks is ¼.

The blind man pulls socks at random. Thus the probability p, that he will pull a white sock is ¾. The probability that he will pull two white socks is $p \times p = p^2 = (¾)^2 = \frac{9}{16}$. Similarly, the probability that he will pull two black socks is $q^2 = (¼)^2 = \frac{1}{16}$. Finally, the probability that he will pull a white sock first and a black sock next is $p \times q = (¾) \times (¼) = \frac{3}{16}$, and that the order of picking will be white first and black next is $q \times p = \frac{3}{16}$. Thus neglecting order, the probability of picking a black and a white sock is $2pq = 2(¾)(¼) = \frac{6}{16}$. If we designate a black sock by B and a white sock by b, we can summarize the results:

black–black	BB	p^2	1/16
black–white	Bb	$2pq$	6/16
white–white	bb	q^2	9/16

To reverse the procedure we observe that on one in 16 days the blind man wears a pair of black socks. Since the combination BB occurs p^2 times, the proportion p of black socks in the drawer is $\sqrt{p^2} = \sqrt{\frac{1}{16}} = ¼$. Similarly, the proportion q of white socks is $\sqrt{q^2} = \frac{9}{16} = ¾$.

Our analogy applies almost directly to population genetics where inferences about the genetic content of gene pools (socks in the drawer) are based on observed frequencies of phenotypes. The analogy is not perfect, because it does not provide for the phenomenon of dominance. Because of dominance, in a large number of genetic conditions there exists no phenotypic difference between a homozygote BB and a heterozygote Bb. Phenotypic and genotypic frequencies do not agree with each other. Only two kinds of phenotypes can be distinguished. This causes some difficulties, but they are easily resolved as the following examples will show.

MONOGENIC TRAITS

Phenylketonuria. Gene frequency within population. At this point the reader is asked to review the earlier discussion on PKU, giving particular attention to the counseling case described there. A young woman, a carrier of the PKU allele, wanted to know what her risk was to marry another carrier. We set the risk at one in 50; that is, we estimated that one in every 50 individuals is a carrier. How did we arrive at this number?

Beginning in 1962, all babies born in Massachusetts hospitals were tested for PKU. The survey indicates that one in every 10,000 babies is a phenylketonuric. We know that PKU is a monogenic recessive disorder, where genotype

> *P1P1 is normal,*
> *P1P2* is a carrier of the recessive allele *P2,*
> *P2P2* is a phenylketonuric.

Let us estimate first the proportions p and q of alleles *P1* and *P2*. Under conditions of random mating, corresponding in our analogy to the "blind" picking of pairs of socks, we expect p^2 *P1P1*, $2pq$ *P1P2*, and q^2 *P2P2* genotypes in the population. We know from the survey that q^2 (the proportion of recessive *P2P2* homozygotes) is 1/10000. It follows that the proportion of alleles *P2* in the gene pool equals $\sqrt{q^2} = \sqrt{1/10,000} = 1/100$. But since the proportion of alleles *P1* and the proportion of alleles *P2* add up to unity ($p + q = 1$), we conclude that $p = 1 - 1/100 = 99/100$.

From here it is only one step to the answer to our original question: How was the estimation arrived at that about one in 50 individuals is a *P1P2* carrier. The proportion of heterozygotes *P1P2* is $2pq$. Substituting the appropriate values, we have $2(99/100)(1/100) = 198/10,000 \approx 200/10,000 = 2/100$, or one in 50.

Differences between Mendelian populations. The incidence of PKU differs from population to population. The value of 1/10,000 (or 10/100,000) was obtained in a survey of newborn babies in Massachusetts. Similar surveys in other countries and in different ethnic and racial groups have yielded different values. In the United Kingdom, the frequency of the disorder is about 4/100,000; in Sweden, it is 2.5/100,000; in Japan, it is 1.7/100,000, and so on. PKU is practically unknown among Jews of European descent, the so-called Ashkenazi. In Israel, PKU was found among Jews, but only among oriental non-Ashkenazi Jews, the so-called Sephardi. Phenylketonuria is also rare among American blacks.

The observation that the incidence of PKU differs from population to population invites a general comment. The frequency of a gene in the gene pool of a population can be computed by the methods described. But the number we derive, the gene frequency, is not a constant of nature as is the speed of light or the boiling temperature of water. It is a variable number (as opposed to a constant) resulting from the historical process we call evolution. Gene frequencies reflect the evolutionary history of a population, including selection pressures to which the population was exposed. Gene frequencies can and do change, although evolutionary changes tend to be slow and barely noticeable when viewed over short periods of time.

Color blindness. *Gene frequency and sex differences.* Earlier in this unit, red-green blindness, a sex-linked condition, was discussed. The symbols X and x were used to designate X chromosomes bearing the dominant and recessive alleles affecting color vision. Normal and abnormal males were XY and xY males, respectively. And normal, carrier, and color-blind females were represented by symbols XX, xX, and xx. It was mentioned that, depending on the population, about five to nine percent of white males are color-blind. These are phenotypic frequencies. How can we estimate gene frequencies from phenotypic frequencies? In the case of sex-linked traits, this is simple. Only two kinds of phenotypic and genotypic males occur in the population. A male can be either normal or he can be color-blind; thus he can be either XY or xY. Consequently, the proportion of normal and color-blind males points directly to the proportion of genotypes XY or xY in the population and to the proportions p and q of alleles X and x in the gene pool. If, for example, $p = 95/100$ and $q = 5/100$, then five percent of all males are color-blind and of genotype xY; and the gene pool of the population contains 5 percent alleles x and 95 percent alleles X.

How much color blindness can be expected in females? Assume we inferred from phenotypic frequencies in males that the gene pool of a population contains 10/100 alleles x $(q = 1/10)$ and 90/100 alleles X $(p = 9/10)$. Under these conditions, the following genotypic frequencies can be expected in females:

Phenotype:	normal	normal	color blind
Genotype:	XX	xX	xx
Frequency:	p^2	2_{pq}	q^2
Frequency if $p = 9/10$ and $q = 1/10$:	81/100	18/100	1/100

Note the following result. In a population in which the frequency of color-blind males is 10 percent (1/10), the frequency of color-blind

TABLE 1.13   FREQUENCY OF COLOR BLINDNESS IN MALES

POPULATION	RACE*	NUMBER	FRE-QUENCY PER-CENT
Fiji Islanders	Melanesian	200	0.0
Brazilian Indians	Amerindian	230	0.0
Bagandas	African	537	1.9
Navaho Indians	Amerindian	163	2.4
Australian natives	Australian	378	3.3
Marshall Islanders	Micronesian	268	4.1
Turks, Istanbul	European	473	5.3
Chinese, Peking	Asian	1,164	6.9
Tonga Islanders	Polynesian	67	7.5
Belgians	European	1,243	8.6
Russians	European	1,343	9.3
V.N.B. Brahmins, Bombay	Indian	100	10.0
Americans	European	803	11.4
Todas, India	Indian	320	12.8
Dutch, Brazil	European	97	15.5
Kotas, India	Indian	28	61.0

* Populations were assigned to one of the nine major races recognized by Garn (1961).

Source: Adapted from Table 19.4 of J. N. Spuhler and G. Lindzey, "Racial Differences in Behavior," in J. Hirsch, ed., *Behavior-Genetic Analysis,* 1967. Copyright 1967 by McGraw-Hill. Used with permission of McGraw-Hill Book Company.

females is one percent: $q^2 = (1/10)^2 = 1/100$. In general, if the phenotypic frequency of an X-linked recessive condition in males is q, the phenotypic frequency in females is q^2. For example, $q = 10/100$, $q^2 = 100/10000$; $q = 5/100$, $q^2 = 25/10000$; $q = 1/100$, $q^2 = 1/10000$. When sex differences were discussed earlier in this unit, it was stated imprecisely that the incidence of color blindness in females is "much lower" than in males. We can now be more precise. We can state the quantitative relationship between the incidence of the condition in males and its incidence in females. In family genetics, we tested the hypothesis about the X-linked, recessive nature of color blindness by a study of pedigrees. In population genetics, we test the same hypothesis by comparing the observed frequency of the condition in males and females. Family studies and population studies complement each other.

Differences between Mendelian populations. The incidence of color blindness has been studied in many populations, and marked differences between populations have been observed, as Table 1.13, adapted from Spuhler and Lindzey (1967), shows. Frequencies for color blindness range from 0 to 16 percent, with one extreme value of 61 percent. Color blindness is clearly more prevalent in European and Indian populations than in the other populations studied. It would be tempting to speculate that normal color vision contributes more to reproductive fitness among food gatherers and hunters, than among pastoral, agricultural, and urban societies, and that this is reflected in Table 1.13. In other words, one could hypothesize that in more primitive societies genes for color blindness are held at low frequencies by natural selection and that in more advanced societies, natural selection against color blindness is relaxed. Consequently, genes for color blindness accumulate in gene pools of more advanced societies. Such a hypothesis would have to be tested using a larger sample of populations than that shown in Table 1.12. In the earlier discussion on color blindness, the reader was warned against easy, although appealing environmental interpretations of behavioral data. It appears equally necessary to warn against facile, although seemingly reasonable evolutionary explanations of differences between populations.

Schizophrenia. *Dominant versus recessive inheritance.* The fact that schizophrenia is a heritable disease is firmly established. But little else is certain about the disorder. Many investigators, as indicated earlier, believe that schizophrenia is a polygenic disorder. Others believe that it results from a recessive gene. Still others, including Heston (1970), attribute schizophrenia to a dominant gene. As a first step in looking at schizophrenia from the viewpoint of population genetics, we will discuss some implications of the dominant and recessive gene hypothesis of schizophrenia.

According to Heston, the current definition of schizophrenia is too narrow. He prefers to talk about "schizophrenic spectrum conditions," since he does not see a clear line of demarcation separating schizophrenics, who were hospitalized for schizophrenia, from schizoids who were never hospitalized but show many symptoms of the disease. If schizophrenics and schizoids are put together, about four percent of the population suffers from the disorder. We will assume that schizophrenia is caused by genes at an autosomal locus S. If the disorder is caused by a dominant gene at this locus, then genotypes SS and Ss are affected, and genotype ss is normal. But if schizophrenia is caused by a recessive gene, then only the double-recessive genotype ss will be affected.

The two hypotheses lead to different estimates of the proportion of alleles S and s in the gene pool of the population:

HYPOTHESIS	AFFECTED	NORMAL	PROPORTION OF SS GENOTYPES
Dominance	SS and Ss	ss	0.96
Recessiveness	ss	SS and Ss	0.04

In the case of dominance the proportion, q, of alleles s in the gene pool is $\sqrt{q^2} = \sqrt{0.96}$ or approximately 0.98; and the proportion of alleles S is $1 - q = 1 - 0.98 = 0.02$. But in the case of recessiveness, the proportion of alleles s is $\sqrt{0.04} = 0.20$; and the proportion of alleles S is $1 - 0.20 = 0.80$. These values lead to the following estimates of genic and genotypic proportions in the population:

HYPOTHESIS	GENIC PROPORTIONS		GENOTYPIC PROPORTIONS		
	p	q	p^2	$2pq$	q^2
Dominance	0.02	0.98	0.0004	0.0392	0.9604
Recessiveness	0.80	0.20	0.6400	0.3200	0.0400

To account for the four percent of schizophrenics and schizoids in the population, the dominance hypothesis assumes that two percent of the alleles at the S locus cause the disorder, namely, the two percent dominant alleles S. To account for the same observed incidence of schizophrenia, the recessive hypothesis must assume that 20 percent of the recessive alleles s in the gene pool of the population are potential causes of the disorder. And regarding genotypes, the dominance hypothesis assumes that about four percent ($0.0004 + 0.0392 = 0.0396 = 3.96$ percent) of the population—the SS and Ss individuals—carry the deleterious allele S in single or double dose, while the recessive hypothesis assumes that $32 + 4 = 36$ percent of the population carries one or two schizophrenia-causing alleles s. This means that according to the dominance hypothesis only four percent of the population can transmit the disorder to the next generation, while according to the recessive hypothesis more than one third of individuals are potential progenitors of affected individuals.

At this point, the reader, having become impatient, may ask what is the practical significance of all such speculations and calculations. We will try to explain one specific area where the theories we discussed have practical implications: eugenics.

Eugenics and schizophrenia. Concern over the population explosion has revived interest in _eugenics, the improvement of the human race by controlled reproduction_. Proponents of eugenic measures argue that it is not enough to pursue a goal of zero-population growth, but that it would be desirable to restrict the reproduction of bearers of unfavorable genes (negative eugenics) and to favor the reproduction of individuals with superior genes (positive eugenics).

Schizophrenia is a prime target for proponents of negative eugenics. They propose to restrict the reproduction of schizophrenics because this would greatly reduce the incidence of schizophrenia. Such a proposal touches on two separate questions. First, shall "improvement of the human race" ever serve as a pretext for restricting anyone's right to reproduce? This is an ethical and political question for which science has no answer. Second, will eugenic measures work, will they appreciably reduce the incidence of schizophrenia? The calculations we undertook help us to give a rational, scientific answer to this second question. The success of a program of negative eugenics would depend on the mode of inheritance of schizophrenia. If schizophrenia is caused by a dominant gene, then about four percent of the population would be affected by restrictions imposed on their reproduction. The program could not be entirely successful because many individuals would reproduce before they developed any symptoms of the disease. But to a degree, it would achieve its goal and reduce the frequency of the dominant gene for schizophrenia, provided, of course, that we were willing to overcome all ethical objections against limiting the civil liberties of our fellow man.

But what if schizophrenia were a recessive disorder? Our calculations indicated that in this case 36 percent of the population would carry at least one of the recessive genes and should forsake having children. With so many individuals affected, it appears utopian to assume that a program of negative eugenics against schizophrenia could be instituted even in the harshest of all totalitarian states. Too many of the enforcers of the law would be affected themselves.

What does this example show? Eugenic measures against various heritable conditions have been proposed often, mostly by individuals genuinely interested in the well-being of man. Eugenic measures often appear reasonable and promise to accomplish their goal. But what appears reasonable on closer analysis may turn out to be unrealistic. The example of schizophrenia shows that, apart from ethical questions, any specific eugenic proposal appears premature. We do not have the facts needed to predict the efficacy of any proposed measure. At present, we do not know whether schizophrenia is caused by dominant or recessive, by one or by many genes. Without such knowledge, the effect of proposed eugenic measures cannot be predicted. The study of the mode of inheritance of a condition is more than an intellectual exercise, it has practical implications.

MULTIFACTORIAL TRAITS

In an earlier discussion, a distinction was made between qualitative and quantitative traits, noting two important facts: (1) Qualitative traits are usually caused by one or two "major" genes; they are monogenic or single-gene traits. By contrast, quantitative traits tend to be caused by many genes, each having only a minor phenotypic effect; quantitative traits, in general, are polygenic traits. (2) Most qualitative traits are not readily modified by environmental factors; for example, bearers of an X-linked gene for color blindness remain color blind no matter what training in color discrimination they receive. Quantitative traits, on the other hand, are environmentally labile; they are shaped by genetic and environmental factors. They are not just "polygenic," but multifactorial traits.

The environmental lability of quantitative traits makes it difficult to study their inheritance. Genetic and environmental contributions are usually confounded. Intelligent parents tend to have intelligent children. But since they not only transmit their genes to the child, but also rear him in an "intelligent" environment, we cannot say whether the IQ of the child is because of his genes or the environment provided by intelligent parents. There are well-documented cases of crime that "runs in families." But does this mean that criminals pass on a "bad seed" to their children or that they set a bad example, which their children imitate?

In discussing ways to disentangle genetic and environmental causes of individual differences earlier, two approaches were arrived at: (1) compare closely related individuals reared in different environments, and (2) compare unrelated individuals reared in the same environment. Data from such studies made it possible to partition the total variance of a trait within a Mendelian population into genetic (h^2) and environmental (e^2) components. We stated, for example, that according to current estimates, in white populations about 75 percent of variation in IQ scores is attributable to heredity ($h^2 = 0.75$) and about 25 percent is attributable to environment ($e^2 = 0.25$). Thus in spite of the usual confounding of genetic and environmental factors, it is possible, by comparison of carefully selected subject groups, to "unravel" these factors.

We are now approaching a much more difficult and largely unsolved problem. It concerns observed differences between Mendelian populations, for example, ethnic groups or races. Suppose Mendelian populations, Alpha and Beta, differ in a quantitative behavioral trait. On the average, Alphas are more anxious, or temperamental, or peaceful, or intelligent than Betas. How do we decide whether the statistical difference between population Alpha and population Beta is because of genetic causes, environmental causes, or both? As members of different Mendelian populations, Alphas presumably differ from Betas genetically. As members of different ethnic groups, they certainly differ from them culturally. Is it the genetic or the cultural difference that accounts for observed behavioral differences?

One way to find out is to compare Alphas and Betas early in life, that is, before they become aware of their racial or ethnic distinctness and before they become indoctrinated in the way of their culture. Examples of two studies using this approach follow.

Temperament of Chinese and American infants. It is common to attribute certain temperamental characteristics to an ethnic group. We have all heard of fiery Irish, impulsive Italians, impassive Orientals, and so on. Are such generalizations justified? Are South Sea islanders placid and good natured, Bavarians jovial, and Spaniards passionate? If so, do such descriptive terms refer to innate or culturally conditioned traits? Daniel G. Freedman and Nina Chinn Freedman (1974) studied this question in nurseries of maternity wards of hospitals in San Francisco and Chicago. The subjects were 24 Chinese-American and 24 European-American newborns examined during their second or third day of life. Test sessions lasted between 30 and 40 minutes during which the Freedmans examined the sensory development, the maturity of the central nervous system, the motor development, the response to social stimuli, and the temperament of the infant. Items measuring temperament distinguished most clearly between Chinese and American infants. For example, when the tester placed a loosely woven cloth over the face of the baby, the typical European-American infant immediately struggled to remove it by swiping with its hands and turning its face. But the typical Chinese-American baby lay impassively, showing few overt motor responses. Similarly, when placed in a prone position, Chinese infants often lay as placed, with their faces flat against the bedding, whereas Caucasian babies turned their faces to the side or tried to lift the head. This maintenance of the face in the bedding can be taken as an example of the relative imperturbability of Chinese infants. There were no significant differences in amount of crying between Chinese and American babies, but Chinese infants almost immediately stopped crying when picked up and spoken to.

The innateness of behavioral differences between ethnic groups is hard to demonstrate. Ethnic groups possess not only unique gene pools, but also unique cultural traditions. To demonstrate genetic causation of group differences, cultural influences must be kept constant or eliminated. This was done by the Freedmans. They tested Chinese-American and European-American babies in the same hospital environment before differing ethnic child-rearing practices could shape the infant's behavior. The Freedman study provides convincing evidence that on the average the two groups differ at birth. The Freedmans stress that while the groups differed statistically, "there was substantial overlap in range on all scales between the Chinese and Caucasian infants." In other words, there were imperturbable Caucasoid and excitable Chinese babies.

Ethnic differences in alcohol sensitivity. It is widely believed that alcoholism is an escape from the stresses of life. According to this belief, no one is born an alcoholic; one becomes addicted to alcohol when overpowered by frustrations. Whatever the merits of the life-stress theory, recent adoption studies show clearly that, other things being equal, some individuals are less likely to become addicted than others. In one study (Goodwin et al., 1973), an experimental and a control group of adoptees was formed. Experimental and control subjects were separated from their biological parents during the first six weeks of life. The two groups differed in one respect only: the probands had an alcoholic parent; the control subjects did not. All subjects, probands and controls, were reared by unrelated adoptive parents; and none had contacts with their real parents. Nevertheless, 10 of the 55 probands (18 percent) were described as "alcoholic" as compared to 4 (5 percent) of the 78 controls. In other words, the probands had nearly 4 times the alcoholism rate of the controls, pointing to a heritable "predisposition" for alcoholism, a fact supported by other studies (Goodwin et al., 1973; Schuckit et al., 1972).

This discussion, however, does not deal with individual, but ethnic predispositions for alcoholism. It is known that the incidence of alcoholism is lower in Mongoloid than in Caucasoid groups. This racial difference is often attributed to social and cultural factors. Wolff (1972) asked whether the difference could not be because of physiological and presumably heritable differences between the races. He had observed that many Mongoloids responded "with a rapid intense flushing of the face and with symptoms of mild to moderate intoxication after drinking alcohol in amounts that have no apparent effect on Caucasoids." This observation led to a more systematic study of randomly selected Caucasoid and Mongoloid men, women, and infants in the United States, Japan, Taiwan, and Korea.

Flushing was determined directly by looking at the face of subjects and, in a more quantitative way, by "optical densitometry of the earlobe," that is, with an electronic light meter. All adults drank beer (5 percent alcohol by volume) and infants were given port wine in sugar water. The amount of alcohol given to adults and infants was adjusted to body weight. During the test, adults were asked to report any subjective symptoms that might be related to drinking.

The study uncovered striking racial differences. Particularly interesting were the differences between infants, because such differences could hardly be attributed to learning. Of 35 Mongoloid infants tested, 26 (74 percent) responded with a visible flush and an increase in optical density of the earlobe, while only one of 20 (5 percent) Caucasoid babies responded that way. The difference was statistically highly significant ($p < .001$).

Wolff demonstrated racial differences in sensitivity to alcohol. Does Wolff's data explain the low incidence of alcoholism in Japanese, Taiwanese, and Koreans? They do not, but they suggest a possible mechanism that may cause some Mongoloids to abstain from drinking. In 1972, Wolff said "The vascular response to drinking and the associated subjective symptoms of intoxication experienced by Mongoloids may prevent many of them from consuming even moderate quantities of alcohol."

That other additional factors must be involved, that the alcohol sensitivity of the autonomic nervous system of Mongoloids do not sufficiently explain the observed difference between some Mongoloids and Caucasoid groups was shown by a follow-up study Wolff undertook in 1973. North American Indians are commonly classified as members of the Mongoloid race. Wolff studied 30 adult members of one American Indian tribe and found that among them the incidence and intensity of flushing in response to alcohol was as great as among the Asian Mongoloids he had studied previously. Yet we know that the incidence of alcoholism in the two groups differs radically. Wolff concluded that "alcoholism is determined by more complex factors than group variations in vasomotor sensitivity to alcohol. Such a biological variation could, however, exercise its effect through interaction with sociocultural forces."

Ethnicity and patterns of mental ability. Previously we discussed several behavioral differences between ethnic groups. We spoke of PKU, color blindness, and temperamental differences between Chinese and American newborn babies. Over the years, reports of many such differences were published; few, however, made the headlines. Nobody seems to care if, say, one ethnic group is found to be less subject to an optical illusion or less sensitive to the bitter taste of phenylthiocarbamide (PTC) than another (Spuhler and Lindzey, 1967). Of all the behavioral differences between ethnic groups, only differing performance on tests of intelligence appears to arouse wide, often passionate interest and continues to be the subject of most intense research (Loehlin et al., 1975).

Table 1.14 and Figure 15 show the results of one representative study (Backman, 1972). Six mental abilities or factors were studied. The tests were standardized to yield for each factor a mean score of 50 and a standard deviation of 10 in a large national sample of predominantly white, non-Jewish high school students. The six factors were: (1) VKN–verbal knowledge, primarily a measure of general

TABLE 1.14 PATTERNS OF MENTAL
ABILITIES IN FOUR ETHNIC GROUPS

GROUP	MENTAL ABILITY					
	VKN	ENG	MAT	VSP	VMS	MEM
Non-Jewish white	51.9(0.3)	51.1(0.2)	52.1(0.3)	51.8(0.2)	49.5(0.4)	50.9(0.3)
Jewish	57.1(0.3)	50.8(0.2)	58.6(0.7)	46.0(0.4)	51.0(0.5)	47.8(0.2)
Black	46.0(0.7)	47.5(0.6)	47.3(0.6)	45.1(0.4)	50.9(0.8)	50.4(0.6)
Oriental	49.0(0.6)	52.5(0.7)	59.1(1.2)	49.4(0.9)	50.3(0.7)	51.6(1.1)

VKN = Verbal knowledge, a measure of general information.
ENG = English, grammar and language usage.
MAT = High school mathematics with a minimum of computation.
VSP = Visual reasoning with spatial forms.
VMS = Visual-motor coordination under speeded conditions.
MEM = Memory, short-term recall of verbal symbols.

Source: Data from M. E. Backman, "Patterns of Mental Abilities: Ethnic, Socio-economic, and Sex Differences," *American Educational Research Journal,* 1972, 9, 1-11. Copyright 1972 by the American Psychological Association. Reprinted by permission. Shown are group means and in parenthesis the standard errors of these means.

information; (2) ENG–English language, grammar and language us-age; (3) MAT–mathematics, high school mathematics, involving a minimum of computation; (4) VIS–visual reasoning, the ability to visualize and mentally manipulate spatial forms; (5) VMS–visual-motor coordination under speeded conditions; and (6) MEM–short-term recall of verbal symbols. Twelfth graders belonging to four ethnic groups (1051 non-Jewish whites, 1236 Jewish whites, 488 blacks, 150 Orientals) were tested.

To gain a fuller understanding of the results shown in Table 1.14, let us compare in detail the data for Jewish (J) and non-Jewish whites (W):

GROUP	VKN	ENG	MAT	VIS	VMS	MEM	AVER-AGE
W	51.9	51.1	52.1	51.8	49.5	50.9	51.2
J	57.1	50.8	58.6	46.0	51.0	47.8	51.9
W–J	−5.2	+0.3	−6.5	+5.8	−1.5	+3.1	−0.7
t	12.3	1.1	8.5	13.0	2.3	8.6	0.6
Probability	<.001	>.05	<.001	<.001	<.05	<.001	>.05

Consider first the average score for groups W and J. The aver-age for W is (51.9 + 51.1 + . . . 52.1 + 51.8 + 49.5 + 50.9)/6 = 51.2. The corresponding value for J is 51.9. Had the six tests been subtests of an intelligence test and had an investigator reported only

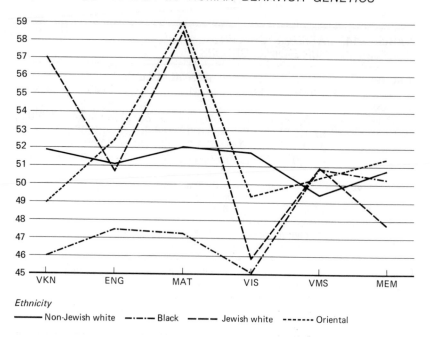

Figure 15. Patterns of mental abilities in four ethnic groups. [After M. E. Backman, "Patterns of Mental Abilities: Ethnic, Socioeconomic, and Sex Differences," American Educational Research Journal, 1972, 9, 1–11.]

the two averages, 51.2 and 51.9, we might have concluded that the two ethnic groups do not differ. Closer inspection of the data and of Figure 15, however, reveal a different picture. The performance of the two groups is equivalent—both achieve almost identical average scores—but the performance is in no way equal. Jewish and non-Jewish whites achieve their equivalent scores by drawing on different talents.

Groups J and W differ significantly on five out of six subtests: J outscores W on three tests and is outscored on two. Only on one test, ENG, the two ethnic groups do not differ significantly. The significance of the difference, W–J, was computed using a statistical process known as t-test. To compute and evaluate t, this formula was used:

$$t = (\text{Mean 1} - \text{Mean 2})/\sqrt{(SE_1^2 + SE_2^2)}$$

All necessary values, means and standard errors (SE), are found in Table 1.14. For example, for populations W and J, and test MEM

$$t = (50.9 - 47.8)/\sqrt{(0.3^2 + 0.2^2)} = 3.1/0.36 = 8.6$$

What does a t of this size tell us? Statistical theory indicates that the probability of obtaining by chance a t larger than 3.3 is less than one in 1000 ($p < .001$). Thus it is improbable that the observed mean difference between W and J was accidental, perhaps because of the fact that by chance only high-scoring subjects were included in group W and only low-scoring subjects were chosen for group J. It is much more likely that some systematic factor operated to cause the observed difference in short-term memory, MEM, between Jewish and non-Jewish whites. The observed difference is significant at the .001 level of confidence.

The results for the other subtests were evaluated similarly, using t values of 2.58 for $p < .01$ and 1.96 for $p < .05$. We see that only on the test for English grammar and language usage the difference between W and J fails to reach statistical significance. Evidently, the composite, average scores for W and J obscured highly significant differences in the intellectual makeup of members of the two ethnic groups.

Table 1.14 presents data for four ($N = 4$) ethnic groups, permitting $N(N - 1)/2 = 6$ group comparisons. Since each group was given six tests, a total of $6 \times 6 = 36$ mean differences can be computed and evaluated. When this is done, we find 13 nonsignificant and 23 (64 percent) significant differences. Of these, two are significant at the .05, five at the .01, and 16 at the .001 level of confidence. Clearly, ethnic groups, like individuals, differ in their intellectual makeup. Each group has its particular mix of strengths and weaknesses.

Why do ethnic groups differ? Environmentalists hold that observed differences are a product of environmental contingencies: ethnic groups often differ in economic status; they almost invariably differ in their culture; they rear their children differently; they instill different values in them. Culture influences intellectual development in a hundred subtle and not-so-subtle ways. Environmentalists feel that all known intellectual differences between ethnic groups can be explained by reference to such economic and cultural differences. Geneticists, on the other hand, believe that genetic differences between ethnic groups may account for some if not all the observed differences. Ethnic groups are Mendelian populations with their own gene pools. Gene exchange occurs primarily between members of the same ethnic group; influx of genes from other groups is restricted. Ethnic groups demonstrably differ with respect to genes affecting morphology, various physiological functions, and some simple behavioral traits. Geneticists do not see why ethnic groups should not also differ with respect to genes affecting higher cognitive functions.

Who is right? Unfortunately, current studies of ethnic group differences are inadequate. Suppose a trait X is studied in two ethnic groups, Alpha and Beta. Alphas are reared in their own cultural environment A; Betas in their environment B:

ETHNIC GROUP	ENVIRONMENT A	B
Alpha	X = 10	
Beta		X = 20

X (*Alpha*) = 10 and X (*Beta*) = 20. How are we to decide whether the observed group difference is because of genotypic differences between Alphas and Betas or to differences between environments A and B? The two factors are inextricably confounded. To separate ethnic-genetic from cultural-environmental factors, a study patterned after adoption studies would be needed. Alphas and Betas would have to be kept ignorant of their ethnic origin and reared in a culture C:

ETHNIC GROUP	ENVIRONMENT A	B	C
Alpha	10		10
Beta		20	20

If in environment C, Alphas and Betas continued to behave "true to form" and continued to be different, we would have evidence for genetic differences between the groups. Studies of this kind have not yet been conducted.

In current discussions of ethnic differences, arguments about the environmental or genetic causes of IQ differences between American blacks and whites are prominent. In all studies of the issue, environmental-cultural and genetic factors are badly confounded, and no prospect exists for the question to be decided soon. Would an adoption study help? Presumably not, because morphological differences between blacks and whites could not be eliminated. Adoptees of either race would be aware of their ethnic origin, and their adoptive parents would share this awareness. Whatever the results of the study, they could again be interpreted in environmental terms (Scarr and Weinberg, 1976).

In short, differences between ethnic groups are not restricted to morphology or so-called simple forms of behavior. Ethnic groups tend to differ intellectually. This fact is firmly established and rarely contested. The current "IQ controversy" deals with the causes of the observed differences. Environmentalists attribute them to cultural and economic factors; geneticists believe that some of the differences are because of heredity. To date, neither side can support its belief with hard data (Loehlin et al., 1975).

REVIEW OF EVIDENCE

All cells of our body descend in direct line from a paternal sperm and a maternal ovum. Enclosed in the nucleus of each cell reside faithful replicas of parental genes and it is widely accepted today that they program and steer the development and growth of our bodies. Do genes also exert some control over our behavior, do they channel and constrain it? There is no longer any doubt that they do. In concluding our brief introduction to human behavior genetics, let us review four lines of evidence for genic control of behavior.

EVIDENCE FROM CHROMOSOME STUDIES

Genes are carried on chromosomes of which we have 23 pairs in every cell of our body. One member of each chromosome pair comes from our father, the other from our mother. Some individuals accidentally receive fewer or more than the normal 2×23 chromosomes from their parents—they inherit an abnormal chromosome set. Almost without exception chromosomal anomaly causes a variety of anatomical defects and physiological malfunctions. With only few exceptions abnormal sets of chromosomes also affect behavior. For example, mongols, individuals suffering from Down's syndrome, have three instead of the normal two chromosomes number 21. As a consequence, many mongols are profoundly retarded, but many are also affectionate, good-natured, and emotionally more stable than most other retarded individuals.

Chromosomal anomalies provide the most tangible evidence for genic control over behavior. Since genes are carried on chromosomes, an abnormal chromosome number leads to an abnormal gene number. In the case of Down's syndrome, if a gene M is located on chromosome 21, then mongols have three copies of that gene. Whatever the normal product of the gene *M* is, mongols have too much of that product, causing their cognitive deficit and, surprisingly, their relative emotional stability.

Mongols are retarded but friendly. Patients with Turner's syndrome (sterile females with one X chromosome) have a peculiar cognitive deficit, though, on the positive side—they tend to face their lot with equanimity. Because of poor impulse control, tall males with two Y chromosomes are overrepresented in prison populations. Clearly, the chromosomal makeup of an individual affects his or her behavior. The microscopic study of chromosomes is in its early stages, but we can expect that with progress in this area, many behavioral differences between individuals will be traced to differences in their chromosomes.

EVIDENCE FROM BIOCHEMICAL STUDIES

Many genes exert their influence through the synthesis of enzymes, organic catalysts of metabolic processes. If gene *A1* synthesizes an enzyme Alpha, but gene *A2* does not, then *A1A1* homozygotes and *A1A2* heterozygotes will synthesize Alpha, but *A2A2* homozygotes will not. If some normal metabolic process requires Alpha, then A2A2 homozygotes, unable to produce the enzyme, will be abnormal, suffering from a genetic disorder of metabolism.

Such biochemical defects often have behavioral concomitants, as the example of phenylketonuria illustrates. Phenylketonurics cannot synthesize phenylalanine hydroxylase, an enzyme that converts phenylalanine to tyrosine. As a consequence phenylalanine, found in a variety of foods, accumulates and is transformed into phenylpyruvic acid and its metabolites. The latter cause damage to the developing brain of patients, resulting in severe mental retardation and a variety of behavioral abnormalities. Patients are hyperactive, noisy, destructive, and given to uncontrollable fits of temper. Some are shy, anxious, and fearful, and, as one observer put it, "none could be described as friendly, placid or happy."

Other heritable disorders of metabolism have different, often quite dramatic, behavioral effects. Patients unable to synthesize HPRT, an enzyme, display symptoms of a disorder known as Lesch-Nyhan syndrome. The enzyme deficiency leads to compulsive self-mutilation by biting away the tongue, lips, and fingertips. Patients also tend to be aggressive. As children they bite and pinch others and learn to swear early. Some have a good sense of humor, but often, quite suddenly and unpredictably, they commit mischievous, even cruel acts against their friends.

The behavior of phenylketonurics and Lesch-Nyhan patients is grossly abnormal. Could it be that other behaviors, less dramatic and less deviant, are caused by other, more benign enzyme deficiencies? Future research will provide answers, but even now the conclusion is inescapable that some genes, through control of biochemical processes, affect behavior. Psychologists are trained to search for psychologically understandable motives of behavior, but, as we see, studies of biochemical genetic causes of behavior can be equally revealing.

EVIDENCE FROM MENDELIAN FAMILY STUDIES

Some behavioral traits "run in families," following a characteristic Mendelian pattern of inheritance; the patterns are typical of autosomal dominant, autosomal recessive, sex-linked dominant, or sex-linked recessive inheritance. For example, Huntington's chorea is clearly and unmistakably an autosomal dominant disease. As is typical of autosomal dominant conditions, the disease does not skip generations, it affects both sexes equally, and it afflicts one-half of the children of patients. In late stages of the disease patients suffer from uncontrollable jerking movements of legs and arms. Frequently, however, the first signs of the disease are changes in the personality of the patient. He becomes irritable, moody, ill-tempered, paranoid, sometimes outright psychotic, requiring hospitalization in a mental hospital. The behavioral symptoms of the disease are indistinguishable from symptoms often thought to be psychological reactions to the stresses of life. Yet, because of the telltale Mendelian way the symptoms "run" in the families of patients, we can be sure that the symptoms have no simple psychological explanation. They may be triggered but they are not caused by environmental forces; they are unquestionably caused by an autosomal dominant gene.

A variety of behaviors and behavioral conditions have been linked to single genes. Some forms of deafness are caused by autosomal recessive genes; color blindness is caused by X-linked recessive genes; and data on inheritance of schizophrenia implicate an autosomal dominant gene. In each case, the inference that the condition is caused by a gene is based on a Mendelian analysis of families. We know, for example, that fathers do not transmit an X-chromosome to their sons. Thus a trait that appears in father and son cannot be X-linked. X-linked recessive traits typically appear in grandfathers, skip a generation, and reappear in grandsons. The daughters of the grandfathers and mothers of the grandsons link the generations; the pattern is unmistakable and leads to the diagnosis of X-linkage.

EVIDENCE FROM CORRELATIONS BETWEEN RELATIVES

Individuals are related to varying degrees. Monozygotic twins share all, parent and child share one-half, uncle and nephew share one-quarter of their genes. Members of the same ethnic group have more genes in common than members of different ethnic groups or members of different races. If genes affect behavior, it should be possible to show that, as a rule, individuals sharing many genes behave more alike than individuals sharing fewer genes. Numerous studies have indeed shown this to be so. Consider the performance of two individuals on an IQ test: if the two are monozygotic twins, their scores, on the average, differ by less than 10 points. If, on the other hand, the two have no close blood ties (to call them "unrelated" would be wrong), their score will, on the average, differ by more than 15 points. Or, consider schizophrenia: if one member of a pair of monozygotic twins is schizophrenic, the odds that the other is also schizophrenic are 1 in 2. In the case of dizygotic twins, the odds are 1 in 10. And if a schizophrenic were matched with a randomly chosen individual, the odds that he too would be schizophrenic are 1 in 100.

When in the past such data were presented, they often came from studies that were methodologically inadequate. Genetic and environmental factors tended to be inextricably confounded in them. For example, twins raised in the same environment were tested so that their scores reflected not only shared genes but also shared environments. In modern behavior-genetic research these factors are dissociated, mostly by comparison of individuals who were separated early in infancy and brought up in different environments. The results of such more recent studies confirm earlier findings—they demonstrate for a whole range of traits that behavioral similarity between family members depends more on shared genes than on shared environments.

What is true of narrowly defined human families is also true of the wider families we call ethnic groups and, encompassing even larger communities of interbreeding individuals, human races. Bone structure and skin color are not the only traits that make for similarity between members of such superfamilies; behavior also contributes to their likeness. Usually such likeness is attributed to the shaping forces of a common culture, but recent research shows that some racial characteristics are present at birth, long before culture had a chance to make an imprint on the developing behavioral characteristics of an individual. Thus, studies of ethnic and racial behavioral differences add to the accumulating evidence for genic constraints on behavior.

We began this inquiry into inheritance of behavior with quotes from Francis Galton (1822–1911), the father of human behavior genetics. Galton was the first hereditarian to "go public," but even today, 100 years after he published his epoch-making treatise on "Hereditary Genius," many social scientists are in no way convinced by his arguments. The battle between hereditarians and environmentalists continues undiminished. On these pages we have presented evidence for inheritance of behavior; the reader will now do well to turn to literature that emphasizes environmental causes of behavioral inequality.

REFERENCES

Axelrod, J. Neurotransmitters. *Scientific American,* 1974, April.

Backman, M. E. Patterns of mental abilities: Ethnic, socioeconomic, and sex differences. *American Educational Research Journal,* 1972, *9,* 1–11.

Dobzhansky, T. A review of some fundamental concepts and problems of population genetics. *Cold Spring Harbor Symposium on Quantitative Biology,* 1955, *20,* 1–15.

————. Species after Darwin. *In* S. A. Barnet (Ed.), *A century of Darwin.* Cambridge, Mass.: Harvard University Press, 1958, 19–55.

Eckland, B. K. Social class structure and the genetic basis of intelligence: An introduction. *In* R. Cancro (Ed.), *Intelligence, genetic and environmental influences.* New York: Grune & Stratton, 1971.

Erlenmeyer-Kimling, L., and Jarvik, L. F. Genetics and intelligence: A review. *Science,* 1963, *142,* 1477–1479.

Freedman, D. G. *Human infancy: An evolutionary perspective.* New York: John Wiley & Sons, 1974.

Galton, F. *Hereditary genius: An inquiry into its laws and consequences.* Cleveland: The World Publishing Company, 1962.

Garn, S. M. *Human Races.* Springfield, Ill., Charles C. Thompson, Publisher, 1961.

Goodwin, D. W., Schulsinger, F., Hermansen, L., Guze, S. B., and Winokur, G. Alcohol problems in adoptees reared apart from alcoholic biological parents. *Archives of General Psychiatry,* 1973, *28,* 238–243.

Guillery, R. W. and Kaas, J. H. Genetic abnormality of the visual pathways in a "white" tiger. *Science,* 1973, *180,* 1287–1289.

Herrnstein, R. I.Q. *The Atlantic Monthly,* 1971, September.

Heston, L. L. Psychiatric disorders in foster home-reared children of schizophrenic mothers. *British Journal of Psychiatry,* 1966, *112,* 819–825.

————. The genetics of schizophrenic and schizoid disease. *Science,* 1970, *167,* 249–256.

Jacobs, P. A., Price, W. H., Court, W. M., Brittain, R. P., and Whatmore, P. B. Chromosome studies on men in a maximum security hospital. *Annals of Human Genetics,* 1968, *31,* 339–358.

Jensen, A. R. How much can we boost IQ and scholastic achievement? *Harvard Educational Review,* 1969(a), *39*(1), 1–123.

————. Reducing the heredity-environment uncertainty. *In* Environment, heredity, and intelligence. *Harvard Educational Review,* Reprint Series No. 2, 1969(*b*), 209–243.

————. IQs of identical twins reared apart. *Behavior Genetics,* 1970, *1,* 133–148.

————. *Educability and group differences.* New York: Harper & Row, 1973.

Juel-Nielsen, N. Individual and environment: A psychiatric-psychological investigation of monozygous twins reared apart. *Acta Psychiatrica et Neurologica Scandinavica* (Monogr. Suppl. 183), 1965.

Kamin, L. J. *The Science and Politics of I.Q.* New York: John Wiley & Sons, 1974.

Knox, W. E. Phenylketonuria. Chapter 11, 266–295, in J. B. Stanbury, J. B. Wyngaarden, and D. S. Frederickson (Eds.), *The metabolic basis of inherited disease.* 3d ed. New York: McGraw-Hill, 1972.

Lejuene, J., Gautier, M., and Turpin, R. Étude des chromosomes somatiques de neuf enfants mongoliens. *Comptes Rendus de l'Academie des Sciences, Paris,* 1959, *248,* 1721–1722.

Li, C. C. A tale of two thermos bottles: Properties of a genetic model for human intelligence. *In* R. Cancro (Ed.), *Intelligence, genetic and environmental influences.* New York: Grune & Stratton, 1971.

Loehlin, J. C., Lindzey, G., and Spuhler, J. N. *Race Differences in Intelligence.* San Francisco: Freeman, 1975.

Meehl, P. Schizotaxia, schizotypy, schizophrenia. *American Psychologist,* 1962, *17,* 827–838.

Money, J. Human behavior cytogenetics: Review of psychopathology in three syndromes—47,XXY; 47,XYY; and 45,X. *Journal of Sex Research,* 1975, *11,* 181–200.

Money, J., and Ehrhardt, A. A. *Man & Woman. Boy & Girl.* Baltimore and London, The John Hopkins University Press, 1972.

Newman, H. H., Freeman, E. N., and Holzinger, K. J. *Twins: A study of heredity and environment.* Chicago: U. of Chicago Press, 1937.

Nielsen, J. Y chromosomes in male psychiatric patients above 180 cm. tall, *British Journal of Psychiatry,* 1968, *114,* 1589–1591.

Nyhan, W. L., Olivier, W. J., and Lesch, M. A familial disorder of uric acid metabolism and central nervous system function. *Journal of Pediatrics,* 1965, *67,* 257–263.

Omenn, G. S. Inborn errors of metabolism: A review of data and of hypotheses. *Behavior Genetics,* 1976, *6,* 263–284.

Rosenthal, D. *Genetics of psychopathology.* New York: McGraw-Hill, 1971.

Sarason, S. B., and Doris, J. *Psychological problems in mental deficiency.* New York: Harper & Row, 1969.

Scarr, S., and Weinberg, R. A. IQ test performance of black children adopted by white families. *American Psychologist,* 1976, *31,* 726–739.

Schuckit, M. A., Goodwin, D. W., and Winokur, G. A study of alcoholism in half siblings. *American Journal of Psychiatry,* 1972, *128,* 122–126.

Shields, J. *Monozygotic twins brought up apart and brought up together.* London: Oxford University Press, 1962.

Silverstein, A. B. An empirical test of the mongoloid stereotype. *American Journal of Mental Deficiency,* 1964, *68,* 493–497.

Slater, E., and Cowie, V. *The genetics of mental disorders.* London: Oxford University Press, 1971.

Snyder, S. H. *Madness and the brain.* New York: McGraw-Hill, 1974.

Snyder, S. H., Banerjee, S. P., Yamamura, H. I., and Greenberg, D. Drugs, neurotransmitters, and schizophrenia. *Science,* 1974, *184,* 1243–1253.

Spuhler, J. N., and Lindzey, G. Racial differences in behavior. *In* J. Hirsch (Ed.), *Behavior-genetic analysis.* New York: McGraw-Hill, 1967.

Stern, C. *Principles of human genetics.* 3d ed. San Francisco: W. H. Freeman and Company, 1973.

Terman, L. M., and Merrill, M. A. *Measuring intelligence,* Boston, Houghton-Mifflin, 1973.

Witkin, H. A., Mednick, S. A., Schulsinger, F., Bakkestrom, E., Christiansen, K. O., Goodenough, D. R., Hirschhorn, K., Lunksteen, C., Owen, D. R., Philip, J., Rubin, D. B., and Stocking, M. Criminality in XYY and XXY men, *Science,* 1976, 193, pp. 547–555.

Wolff, P. H. Ethnic differences in alcohol sensitivity. *Science,* 1972, *175,* 449–450.

———. Vasomotor sensitivity to alcohol in diverse mongoloid populations. *The American Journal of Human Genetics,* 1973, *25,* 193–200.

HOW WE SEE: THE VISUAL SYSTEM
UNIT TWO

GERALD H. JACOBS
University of California, Santa Barbara

INTRODUCTION TO THE VISUAL SYSTEM

It is not surprising that man commonly uses the phrase "I see" to indicate that he comprehends something for, as in other primates, behavior in our own species is centrally dependent on the use of environmental information gathered by our eyes and processed by our visual systems. But vision, the process of seeing, is such an intimate feature of our experience that we nearly always take it completely for granted. Often it is only in those cases where vision fails in some way, from something as simple as entering a darkened room to something as tragic as the onset of blindness, that we become aware of the overwhelming importance of the visual sense.

Interest in understanding vision and the visual system is not new. The productive scientific study of vision is, in fact, well over two centuries old and the names of many of the geniuses of modern science are associated with this endeavor. Because it has attracted the attention of many, the facts and theories about our primary sensory system fill many books and cover thousands of pages in dozens of scientific journals. But despite the fact that we do know much about vision, the visual system still seems at times almost infinitely complex and thus many of its aspects, even today, remain obstinately mysterious. In this unit some of the features of vision will be explored. Obviously, in a field of endeavor as large as this one, not all possible topics can be covered in a short space. What we will do is concentrate on some of the basic aspects of seeing. The hope is that sufficient information will be conveyed to permit you to become a little more familiar with an almost-miraculous process, which at this very moment, requires the concerted and subtle cooperation of millions of cells in your visual system.

A brief explanation about the approach used. In the study of sensory systems, much more than in most other areas of psychology, the artificiality of the boundaries between scientific disciplines has been widely recognized. What we know of sensory systems results from the combined efforts of anatomists, physiologists, behaviorists, and others. There has been an immensely fruitful interchange of methods and results from a variety of different kinds of scientific attacks—behavioral results often lead to predictions about physiological organizations, structural descriptions frequently suggest behavioral interpretations, and so on. Thus, as you will see, the material presented here was obtained from a variety of different scientific viewpoints. To answer the question of how we see, it is clear that we must draw from as wide a range of relevant information as is possible.

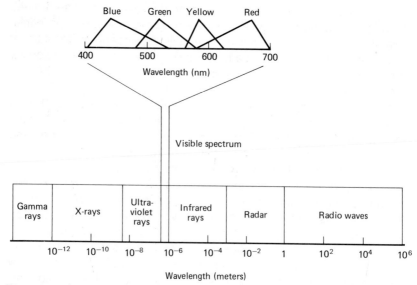

Figure 1. *Types of electromagnetic radiation arranged by wavelength. The color names given at the top are those normally associated with the enclosed bands of wavelengths.*

PHYSICAL AND ANATOMICAL BASIS FOR VISION

To understand vision, it is necessary to know a little of the circumstances that provide for vision and something about the structure of the device that makes vision possible. In other words, we must briefly discuss the stimulus for vision and some of the basic features of the organization of the visual system.

THE STIMULUS

What permits us to see? Of course, light. But it is a good deal easier to say that than it is to explain what light is. For centuries scientists have sought for and argued about the nature of light. Here it is sufficient to consider light as a stream of energetic particles (*quanta*) traveling at immense speed (just under 300,000 kilometers per second). These particles propagate as an oscillating wave. The distance between successive peaks of the wave is called the *wavelength*. Light is only one of the several forms of electromagnetic radiation. All such radiations can be categorized according to their wavelengths. Figure 1 illustrates the various types of electromagnetic radiations arranged according to their wavelengths. It is clear that our visual systems are able to make use of only a small fraction of the total range of electromagnetic radiations. But they do so with amazing efficiency.

How is light specified as a stimulus for vision? One important dimension is the number of light quanta coming from any spatial location per unit of time. This is commonly called the intensity of the light. A second dimension derives from the fact that not all light is qualitatively the same—it differs in wavelength. In Figure 1 you can see that vision is possible only when the radiation comes from a range of about 400–700 nm (a namometer—nm—is 10^{-7} or 0.0000001 centimeters). Note that the wavelengths of 450–500 nm normally appear bluish, those from about 570 nm yellowish, those from 625–700 nm reddish, and so on. This sort of display is called a spectrum; and like a rainbow, it is commonly described in terms of its various colors. However, it is essential to remember that the properties that permit you to call a light of 570 nm "yellow" are in your visual system. Color, like beauty, is in the eye (and the visual system) of the beholder.

Where does light come from? It is emitted by both natural sources (like the sun) and by artificial sources (like your desk lamp). All other objects either absorb light or reflect it, and almost all do both. Thus it is possible to describe a visual stimulus by its physical location (since light quanta typically travel along straight lines from the source), by its intensity (the number of quanta emitted or reflected per unit of time), and by its quality (the relative numbers of quanta having various wavelengths).

THE EYE

The eye is an extraordinary device. Its operation permits us to select from among the welter of available quanta at each instant and to initiate a process that results in visual experience. Furthermore, it does so continuously over an enormous range of constantly fluctuating stimulus conditions. Figure 2 shows a schematic representation of a horizontal cross section of a human eye. The eye is roughly spherical in shape. Light enters through a covering at the anterior surface of this sphere (the *cornea*), passes back through the *aqueous humor,* the *lens,* the *vitreous humor,* and then into the *retina.* The cornea, the lens, the aqueous and vitreous humor are all transparent. The retina is the location in the eye where light has its initial interaction with the nervous system. One major form of information processing goes on before light encounters the retina. Both the cornea and the lens bend (*refract*) the rays of light entering the eye. Refraction occurs when light passes between two media that do not have the same optical densities. The net effect of the refractions in the eye is to form a sharp image of the external visual stimulus on the retinal surface. The degree to which the cornea participates in this process can be appreciated by recalling what it is like to open one's eyes

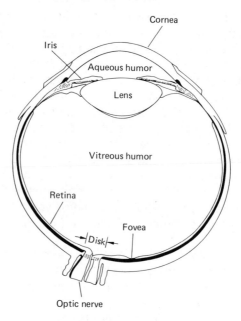

Figure 2. *Schematic cross section of the human eye. The view is that produced by a horizontal cut through the right eye.*

under water, because then the normal refractive power of the cornea is lost. And so is much of the acuteness of normal vision.

The lens has an additional interesting property. This is that the shape of the lens can be altered by changes in the contraction of the ciliary muscle. Changes in lens shape result in changes in the lens refractive power. Such a change is equivalent to moving a lens closer or further from the surface on which light is imaged, much like one does in focusing a camera. To put it correctly, the lens has a variable focal length. This change in lens shape is called *accommodation* and is normally carried on automatically. The usual stimulus to accommodation is the appearance of a visual stimulus in front of the eye. Within about one-third of a second the lens adjusts in shape according to the distance of the object from the eye to bring the object into sharp focus on the retina. The ability to accommodate the lens is progressively lost through age as the lens hardens so that by age 40–50 it is no longer possible to bring about much change in lens shape by activation of the ciliary muscle. Defects of the cornea and lens are common. Box 1 describes common defects of the cornea and lens.

One other interesting feature of the preretinal optical system is the *iris,* the circular muscle located in front of the lens. Constriction or dilation of this muscle causes a change in the size of

---

BOX 1

COMMON DEFECTS OF THE LENS AND CORNEA

1. If a refracting object such as a lens does not have the same curvature in all directions, it is called *astigmatic*. It is not uncommon for the human lens or cornea to suffer this defect, that is, for the curvature to become slightly different in one direction from what it is in another. The effect of this asymmetry is to cause a special sort of blurring of any images formed by the structure. The nature and degree of astigmatism can be assessed clinically by having the patient view an array of lines all arranged at different angles like this:

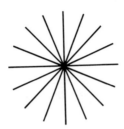

An astigmatic patient will see some of these lines sharply focused; others (located at right angles) will be badly blurred; the remainder will fall somewhere between badly blurred and sharply focused. Once the angle and extent of the astigmatism is known, it is possible to provide eyeglasses with lenses that compensate for the astigmatism and thus bring all lines in the test pattern into crisp focus. Of those who need to wear prescription lenses, a substantial fraction have an astigmatic condition. If you wear glasses you can tell if you are astigmatic by holding the lenses away from your face and rotating the glasses. If the lenses are ground to correct for an astigmatism, the objects you view through the lens will distort in length as you rotate the glasses.

2. Ideally, the optical system in the eye forms a sharp image on the retina. If the image is not sharp, it may be either because the image is being formed in front or in back of the plane of the retina. If you are lucky (and it helps to be young) your lens and cornea focus the external world appropriately on the retina. If so, your eye is said to be *emmetropic*. If, however, images are formed a little in front of the retina your eye is *myopic* (nearsighted); if the image is formed behind the plane of the retina the appropriate term is *hypermetropic* (farsighted). Both conditions are common and in the usual instance may be corrected by the wearing of external lenses that either increase the refractive power of your eye if you are hypermetropic or decrease the refractive power of the eye if you are myopic. The causes of these common defects may involve changes in the refractive powers of the lens or cornea, or it may be that the length of the eye from anterior to posterior is abnormal, or

there may be some combination of both of these problems. There is some evidence that extensive viewing of close objects contributes to the onset of myopia, an affliction common to those who indulge in heavy reading or too much needlepoint.

the aperture, the *pupil,* through which light must pass into the lens. Pupil size is also automatically regulated. The usual conditions leading to changes in pupil size are changes in the amount of available light. In low light, pupil size becomes very large; in bright light, the pupil becomes small. One good place to see this relationship is among primarily nocturnal animals, like the domestic cat. These animals show especially striking changes in pupil size. In man, the pupil varies in size from a diameter of about 2 millimeters in bright light to a diameter of about 8 millimeters in dim light. Circumstances other than changes in light levels can also cause a change in pupil size. For example, strong emotional states will cause an enlargement of pupil size. A variety of drugs also cause changes in pupil size. The alteration in pupil size has two consequences—it grossly regulates the amount of light passing into the eye, and it affects the degree to which a high quality image can be formed on the retina. In general, as with the aperture of a camera, the larger the pupil size, the poorer the quality of the image produced on the retina.

THE RETINA

As you can see in Figure 2, the retina lines the inner surface of the posterior two-thirds of the eyeball. It is the location where incoming light is altered into an energy form that can be processed and transmitted through the visual system. The structure of this delicate tissue is complex in detail, but the outlines are simple. Figure 3 schematizes some of the important classes of cells that make up the retina. The key to the retina is the *photoreceptor.* A receptor is a device that receives and converts one form of energy to another. In this case, the conversion is from the energy of a light quantum to the electrochemical change used as a signaling device by the nervous system. Curiously, the photoreceptors are located at the backmost portion of the retina, the farthest from the incoming light.

The photoreceptors are marvelously efficient at carrying out their functions. To do so they contain *photopigments.* Each photoreceptor contains millions of molecules of photopigment. *Pigments* (for example, dyes of various kinds) are composed of molecules that absorb light. For most pigment molecules, the energy from

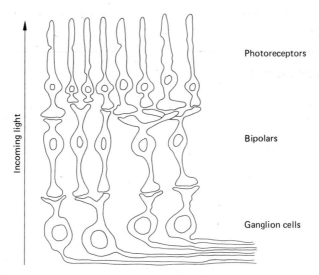

Figure 3. *Schematic drawing of the cells of the retina. The actual numbers of cells and the complexity of their interconnections are greatly over-simplified.*

absorbed light leads to a tiny increase in the temperature of the pigment and nothing else. But in photopigments, absorption of light leads to a rapid change in the chemical configuration of the photo-pigment molecule that eventually results in a signal being delivered to the visual system. Different photopigments are characterized by the degrees to which they are able to absorb light of different wave-lengths: some absorb light most efficiently in some parts of the spectrum while others absorb light most efficiently in other parts of the spectrum.

In many mammalian eyes, including those of man, there are two types of photoreceptors. They are called *rods* and *cones,* mostly because of their characteristic shapes. Human rods and cones differ in several ways. Probably most important is that they contain different photopigments. The photopigment contained in human rods absorbs light having a wavelength of about 500 nm most efficiently. There are three different types of cones each containing a different kind of photopigment. (We will have more to say about this feature later on.) Another difference between the rods and the cones is that their numbers and spatial distributions in the retina differ. Each human retina contains about 120 million rod photoreceptors and about 6 million cone photoreceptors. In Figure 2 you will see that there is an indentation in the central part of the retina, the *fovea.* This is where the image of a fixated object falls. The only photoreceptors present in the center of the fovea are the cones. Outside the fovea the number of cones per unit area decreases until their density becomes small at

BOX 2

ENTOPTIC EFFECTS

Some of the unusual structural properties of the eye give rise to observable visual effects. Because these perceptual effects arise within the eye, they are referred to as *entoptic*. You might find it interesting to verify for yourself two such effects.

1. THE BLIND SPOT

Recall from Figure 2 that the peripheral processes of the ganglion cells are all gathered in a bundle and depart the eye at the optic disc. At this point, there is no room for photoreceptors. Since there are no photoreceptors, any light that falls in this region cannot contribute to vision. Therefore, the visual field contains a blind region (a *scotoma*) corresponding to the location of the optic disc. The presence of the blind spot is easily verified. To do so, close your left eye; and with your right eye fixated on some point, move a small object (like the head of a pencil) around in an area to the right and slightly below that of the object you are fixating. At some location the head of the pencil will disappear. At that point the image of the pencil head is falling directly on the optic disc. If you wish, you can do this more formally and get a measurement of the size and configuration of the blind spot and its relationship to the point of fixation (the fovea). If you place a fixation point at a measured distance from your eye and plot (by drawing) the outlines of the blind spot accurately, then, with a bit of trigonometry, you can find the angular relationship between the fovea and the optic disc. (You should find that the blind spot location is about 13–14° from the fixation point and about 2–3° below it). The reason we are not normally aware of this substantial defect in our visual world is that an object whose image falls on the optic disc in one eye does not fall on the optic disc in the other eye. Hence one must close an eye to observe it.

2. MAXWELL'S SPOT

In man there is a yellow pigment in front of the photoreceptors in the central part of the eye. Like all other pigments, this pigment absorbs some light which would normally reach the photoreceptors. Since it appears yellow, this means the pigment absorbs light most strongly in the short wavelengths. And since the pigment covers only a restricted portion of the retina, this means a colored light should appear differently, depending on whether it passes through the pigmented area or falls on an adjacent region without pigment. To see Maxwell's spot, get two color filters, a blue one and a yellow one. (Your school's psychology department should have the filters.) Stare alternately through these two filters at a brightly lighted white surface, such as a white sheet of paper. As you look through the blue filter, you should see a small dark ring around the point of fixation. This is Maxwell's spot and indicates the location of the yellow pigment in your retina. The ring will fade fairly quickly, but may be reinstituted by staring for a period of time through the yellow filter before going back to the blue filter.

the extreme periphery of the retina. At the same time, the number of rods increases as you move away from the fovea. Obviously, then, the ratio of rods to cones affected depends on which portion of the retina the light falls on.

The photoreceptors form neural connections (*synapses*) with cells lying directly beneath them, the *bipolars* (see Figure 3). These cells in turn connect to cells lying in another layer of the retina. These latter cells are called *ganglion cells.* The total number of ganglion cells in each human retina is about 1 million. Since there are many times this number of photoreceptors, it is clear that the effects from many photoreceptors must influence each ganglion cell. The number of photoreceptors influencing each ganglion cell again depends on the part of the retina viewed. Near the fovea, the ratio between receptors and ganglion cells is low (that is, the output from only a small number of photoreceptors influence each ganglion cell). But as you move toward the retinal periphery, the number of photoreceptors per ganglion cell becomes high. The point of all this is that the topography of the retina is not homogeneous and thus one should expect that the functional characteristics of the retina depend on just where the light falls on the retina (see Box 2).

CENTRAL VISUAL SYSTEM

The peripheral processes of the ganglion cells course across the surface of the retina and are gathered into a compact bundle at the *optic disc* (Figure 2). This bundle forms the optic nerve, the communication channel by which the eye "speaks" to the rest of the visual system. The detailed anatomy of the central visual system is complicated. Figure 4 shows in schematic form the major features of the central visual system. The optic nerves from the two eyes interdigitate at the *optic chiasm* so that fibers arising from the nasal part of the retina cross toward the other side of the brain whereas fibers arising from the temporal half of each retina do not cross. Beyond the chiasm, the fiber bundle is called the *optic tract.* The fibers in each optic tract synapse with cells in the *lateral geniculate nucleus.* The processes of cells in these structures pass to the *visual cortex,* a region located at the posterior pole of the brain. The visual cortex is comprised of at least three successive levels (Areas 17, 18, 19) with

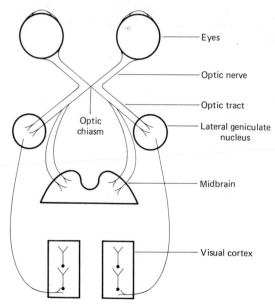

Figure 4. *Representation of the structure of the visual system. The relationships are schematically correct, but anatomically inaccurate with regard to distances and sizes.*

visual information being fed from one to another. In addition to the pathways from the eye to the visual cortex, a second limb of the visual system sends fibers to a variety of structures located in the midbrain.

VISUAL SENSITIVITY

A measurement of sensitivity involves an assessment of the capacity of a device to respond to stimulation. In the case of the visual system, sensitivity measurements are often carried out for purely practical purposes—for example, to determine how intense a signal light must be for it to be easily perceptible under some set of conditions or to find out how large the letters must be on a highway sign to be easily read by a passing motorist. Sensitivity measurements are also often made to permit scientists to draw some inferences about the nature of the mechanisms which underlie the capacity. Dozens of aspects of visual sensitivity have been measured in a large number of experiments. Some of these aspects are considered in the following pages.

THRESHOLDS

In a typical measurement of visual sensitivity, some feature of the visual stimulus is systematically changed while all other features

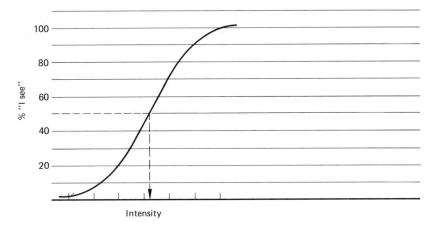

Figure 5. *Measurement of visual threshold.*

are kept the same. The subject is requested to give some judgment about the visual stimulus and a record is kept of how his judgment changes as a function of the changes in the stimulus. The aspect he might be required to judge could be something as simple as the presence or the absence of a light. Or it could involve making some comparative judgment about two or more stimuli present at the same time; for instance, whether the stimuli appear the same or different. In either case, the experimenter will end up with a scale of recorded judgments corresponding to the physical changes he has made in the visual stimulus. Consider an actual example. Suppose the subject is instructed to fixate (stare at) some location in visual space and is told that periodically a tone will sound and at the same time a light may appear in the fixated location. His task is to say on each occasion of the tone whether he sees the light. If the experimenter varies the intensity of the light from presentation to presentation and if the subject is reliable, the experimenter will obtain an outcome like that shown in Figure 5 where the average percentage of "I see" responses is plotted against the intensity of the light. Note that the subject transits smoothly from never seeing the light to seeing it all the time as intensity is increased. Conventionally, some set level of performance is selected by the experimenter (in this case 50 percent) The physical value of the stimulus (in this case the intensity) required to produce this criterion level of performance is called the *threshold.* The procedure is obviously arbitrary and not without problems (for example, it is difficult to be sure that the subject is using the same aspect of the light to detect its presence on each occasion), but it does permit systematic assessments of sensory capacity.

Probably the most basic measurement of visual sensitivity involves an attempt to find out the least amount of light a human can detect. Although this may sound like a straightforward measurement, it is in practice a difficult experiment to perform as many features of the experiment need to be precisely specified. For example, one must be sure that all of the light falls on the same portion of the retina on successive trials, that the subject is always fully prepared to view the stimulus, and so on. When these requirements are adequately satisfied, the truly remarkable sensitivity of the human eye is revealed. It turns out that under ideal conditions a human viewer reaches the "I see" threshold when about 100 quanta fall on the cornea. Low as this figure is, the final picture is even more impressive, since, of the 100 quanta reaching the cornea, only about half a dozen will actually affect molecules of photopigment in the receptors. Furthermore, given the size of the retinal area over which this light is spread, it can be calculated that no single photoreceptor is apt to be hit by more than one quantum of light. This implies that a single quantum is sufficient to activate a single photoreceptor and that only about six of these events need occur at about the same time for vision to ensue. Given that the quantum is an indivisibly small amount of energy, it is apparent that, at the limit, our visual systems are about as sensitive as they could possibly be.

ADAPTATION

As we have seen, the eye is capable of responding to a tiny amount of light. The situation in which this measurement was made involved placing the subject in complete darkness and presenting feeble flashes of light. It certainly is reasonable to ask the opposite question: what is the maximal amount of light under which functional vision is still possible? Strictly speaking, this is impossible to determine since very high light levels can produce physical damage to the eye and thus it would be foolhardy to try and measure an upper limit. Nevertheless, it is clear that the total range of intensity over which the visual system operates is large. Vision is certainly still possible at intensity levels that are 10 billion times[1] as intense as that minimal amount of light needed to see in complete darkness. This is a truly staggering range of light intensities. It gives another indication of the versatility of the visual system as a device to analyze light.

Consider for a moment the difficulty involved in building a physical device that operates over a total intensive range as large as the one that the visual system faces. A major problem is that the device (like the visual system) must not only be able to operate over a large range of intensities; but at any given intensity level, it must also be sensitive to slight changes in intensity. To put it properly, the device needs both a large sensitivity range and good differential sensitivity. There are two obvious ways to build a device to satisfy these two requirements. One is to have in the device many com-

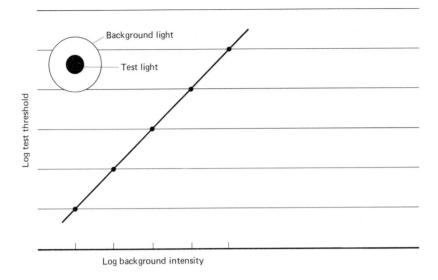

Figure 6. *Results of visual threshold measurements. The inset shows the experimental situation. The intensity of the background light is plotted on the horizontal axis. The vertical axis shows the measured threshold for the test light at each intensity of the background light.*

ponents each of which only operates over a restricted intensity range, but with high sensitivity over that range. This is an inefficient way to accomplish the goal as it means there would have to be an enormous number of components, the majority of which are only activated infrequently. The other way to build a device having a large absolute range and good differential sensitivity is to provide a means by which it is possible to continuously change the sensitivity of the components—to make them more sensitive when there is little light and less sensitive when much light is present. The second scheme is the one primarily employed by the visual system. The process that continuously adjusts the sensitivity of the visual system in accord with how much light is present is called *adaptation*.

To get a more explicit understanding of what adaptation means, Figure 6 should be examined. This figure shows some visual thresholds measured at a variety of different light levels. The experiment in which these measurements were made is straightforward. The subject looks at a large circular area of light (the background), which is continuously present. A smaller (test) region (illustrated in the inset of Figure 6) is illuminated for brief periods of time, and its intensity is varied to permit a measurement of threshold. This procedure is repeated several times, each time with a different amount of light in the large circle. As Figure 6 shows, when one puts more light in the large circle, the measured threshold increases, that is, the sensitivity of the visual system decreases. This is *adaptation*. Note that the degree of change in threshold is roughly proportional to the light level at which the threshold is measured; that is, for a one-unit change in the amount of light in the large circle, the threshold also changes about one unit. If one moves toward the right in the figure, the decrease in sensitivity of the eye observed is called *light adaptation;* the increase in sensitivity seen as one moves to the left is called *dark adaptation.*

Since we live in a world of constantly changing light levels, dark and light adaptation are not exotic laboratory demonstrations, but are at the core of how we see. Of course, adaptation takes time. The situation in which we are most aware of visual adaptation is one in which we move rapidly between extremes in light levels. If you walk from a sunlit afternoon into a darkened theater, you become effectively blind. You might initially suppose this enormous insensitivity is because of little light being in the theater. You soon find, however, that this is not the complete explanation because after a few minutes in the theater you can see again, even though, obviously, the amount of light in the theater has not increased. What has changed is the sensitivity of your visual system, you have become dark adapted. If you move in the other direction, the effect is not nearly as obvious. Although you may experience some insensitivity as you go from the theater back into the sunlight, it is of short duration. Thus although it is possible to represent both dark and light adaptation along a single dimension (as was done in Figure 6), the time courses of the two processes are substantially different with light adaptation being much the faster.

Figure 7 shows a more usual representation of the process of dark adaptation. To generate data of this kind, the eye is first exposed to a bright light for some period of time. The light is then extinguished and the minimum amount of light required to reach visual threshold is measured at various times after the light was turned off. The result is called a dark-adaptation curve. Note that the total drop in threshold is substantial—in this case threshold decreases by about 100,000 times (five log units)—and that it takes 30 to 45 minutes to achieve this total change. Also note that the curve has two clearly discernible segments. The first of these segments has a time course of about 10 minutes; the second is substantially longer. Through many different kinds of observations it has been shown that the first portion of this curve is because of changes in sensitivity in the cone photoreceptors, while the second portion is known to be because of the operation of the rod photoreceptors. The total increase in sensitivity attributable to the cones amounts to about two log units. Also note that the time course of dark adaptation is faster for the cones than for the rods. These differences, as well as many others, have led

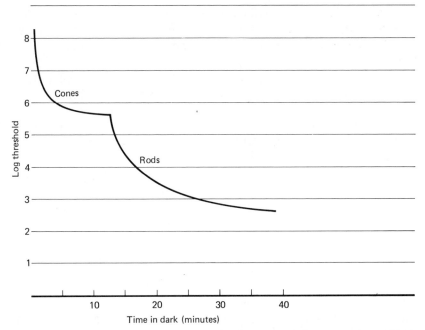

Figure 7. *Dark adaptation curve. The first segment is because of sensitivity changes in the cones, while the second segment results from changes in the sensitivity of the rods.*

scientists to the conclusion that the rods and the cones comprise two different portions of the visual system. This idea of a visual system with two functionally differentiable components is frequently referred to as *visual duplicity.*

The basic features of visual adaptation can be simply summarized by noting that the threshold for vision depends on the preceding history of light stimulation. If the eye has been exposed to bright lights, its sensitivity will be low (high threshold). If the eye has been exposed to dim light, its sensitivity will be high (low threshold). The dynamic processes that change sensitivity in accord with the prevailing light conditions are called dark and light adaptation.

SOME MECHANISMS FOR VISUAL ADAPTATION

The mechanisms that produce visual adaptation are still not completely understood despite much work on the problem. We have already described one device that has something to do with the control of visual sensitivity: change in pupil size. Obviously, when pupil size is large, more light can enter the eye than when the pupil is tightly constricted. Excluding light when much of it is available is certainly one means of desensitizing the eye during light adaptation. However, it can be shown that the total range of adaptation that can be achieved by changes in the size of the pupil is many times smaller than the total range of adaptation actually seen in the human visual system. Clearly one must look beyond the pupil for an understanding of the mechanisms for visual adaptation.

It is, in fact, the photopigment of the retinal photoreceptors that has attracted the greatest attention as a possible mechanism for adaptation. This is not hard to understand. We have already pointed out that the energy from a single quantum can be absorbed by a molecule of photopigment. There has been intensive study of the behavior of the retinal photopigments, mostly in recent years; and consequently much is known about the dynamics of this activity. This is particularly true for the photopigment contained in mammalian rods, a pigment called *rhodopsin.* The essentials are that absorption of a quantum of light by a molecule of photopigment initiates in the molecule a complicated train of events (since absorption of light causes a change in the color of the photopigment the process is called *bleaching*). One effect of these events is to cause a photoreceptor to provide an electrical signal, which may then be communicated to the rest of the visual system. Another consequence is that the molecule becomes temporarily unresponsive to other quanta of light. Obviously, the more quanta present, the more molecules of photopigment are bleached and temporarily unresponsive.

With this much information it is probably easy for you to see why early scientists thought it possible to explain all visual adaptation simply as a result of photopigment bleaching. The story would go as follows: with the eye in darkness, very few molecules of photopigment would be in a bleached state, hence any incoming quanta would be likely to strike some unbleached photopigment molecules and cause an excitation of the visual system. On the other hand, in very bright light many photopigment molecules would be in a bleached state at any given time and hence the number of unbleached molecules available to capture incoming quanta would be small. In the former case one would expect high sensitivity, while in the latter, low sensitivity should occur. The same general idea also seemed to predict some quantitative relationships—for example, bleaching away half of the photopigment molecules should double the threshold. Like so many other cases in science, this appealingly simple idea has turned out to contain both correct and incorrect aspects.

It has only been in about the last twenty years that visual scientists have been able to measure directly the amount of photopigment in a bleached state in the intact human eye. The results of such measurements show that there is a consistent relationship between the amount of photopigment in a bleached state and visual threshold. Figure 8 details results from an experiment involving simultaneous measurement of visual threshold and the proportion of

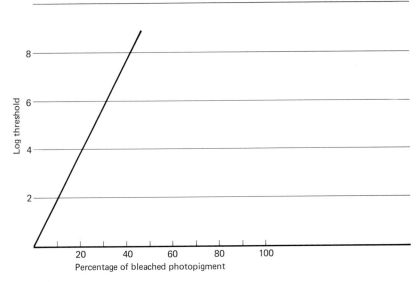

Figure 8. *Relationship between visual threshold and the amount of bleached photopigment for human scotopic vision. Note that there are very large changes in visual threshold for relatively small changes in the amount of photopigment in the bleached state.*

bleached photopigment in a human eye. Note that threshold increases smoothly as the proportion of bleached pigment increases. This is certainly what one would expect based on the kind of arguments given in the previous paragraph. But the graph also shows that the predicted quantitative relationship is wrong. Recall that we expected that halving the amount of unbleached photopigment would double the threshold, but actually such a change in bleached photopigment leads to an enormous change in threshold. (This is a bit tricky, but of importance here is that the axis on which threshold is plotted has been greatly compressed by plotting it logarithmically. If this still seems opaque, it might help to point out that doubling or halving something is equivalent to a change of 0.3 log units.) The essential point of experiments of this kind is that one measures large changes in visual sensitivity for small changes in the proportion of photopigment in the bleached state.

In addition to troubles with the predicted quantitative relationships, it has also become clear that other facts do not fit comfortably with the idea that visual adaptation effects can be attributed solely to changes in retinal photopigments. Perhaps the most persuasive of these facts is that the desensitizing effect of a light depends on its spatial structure as well as on its intensity. It has been known for many years that the characteristics of a dark adaptation curve (like that shown in Figure 7) depend on the size of the area of the retina

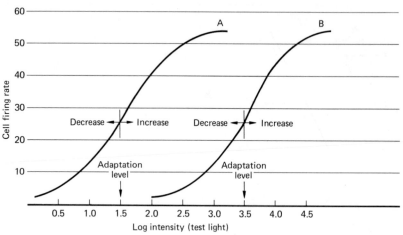

Figure 9. *Results from two experiments (A & B) illustrating the effects of visual adaptation on the responses of a single cell in the visual system. In each case, the adaptation level refers to the intensity of the light to which the eye is adapted. The curves show the response of the cell to brief increases and decreases in light from these adaptation levels.*

illuminated in measuring the threshold. Thus threshold is lowered as the area illuminated by the light is made larger. Spreading the light over a larger area should not affect the amount of photopigment bleached in any single retinal location, and so it is clear that some aspects of adaptation must be based on events occurring beyond the retinal receptors. Because of results like these there has been a good deal of work in recent years directed toward attempting to specify the relative contributions of "photopigment" and "neural" adaptation. The issues so far are very complex but it is clear that the final understanding of visual adaptation will have to include a description of multiple mechanisms—photopigment events surely, but also events occurring at many locations in the visual nervous system.

Finally, let us look briefly at the characteristic behavior of the visual nervous system during adaptation. Single cells in nervous systems communicate with one another by means of electrical signals. One characteristic form of such signal is a brief, unitary event called an *action potential.* Nerve cells produce such action potentials aperiodically and signal information through either increases or decreases in the rate of action potentials. The means by which such signals convey visual information has been intensively investigated, particularly during the last decade.

Consider the behavior of a nerve cell in the visual system during a typical experiment on visual adaptation. Figure 9 shows the frequency of action potential discharge for the cell as a function of the intensity of light falling on the retina. We first permit the eye to adapt to some steadily presented light (the adaptation level). In Figure 9 (A) the cell discharges (fires) about 25 times per second when the eye is completely adapted to the steady light. Next the light is *briefly* increased or decreased in intensity from the adaptation level. For this particular nerve cell, as the light is increased the frequency of action potentials also goes up; as the light is decreased in intensity the frequency of action potentials goes down. Furthermore, the degree of change can be seen to depend on how much the intensity of the light has been changed. Thus in curve (A), for a one-log unit increase in light intensity, the cell's discharge rate goes up to 50/second; for a one-log unit decrease in light intensity, the cell's rate drops to about 5/second. Thus when the intensity of the light is changed to levels that are fairly close to the adaptation level, the cell's output changes sharply and systematically—it has good differential sensitivity. However, if the light is briefly changed in intensity by more than about one log unit there are no further changes in firing rate. That is, the cell is unable to signal differentially between, say, 1.2 and 2.0 log units. This is similar to how the whole visual system behaves—brief changes of intensity over a range of about plus and minus one log unit from an adaptation level lead to highly perceptible changes in the appearance of a light (it becomes brighter or darker). Changes beyond the limits of about plus or minus one log unit do not lead to much further change in the appearance of the light (it does not become substantially brighter or darker). Thus the behavior of the individual visual cell mimics in a qualitative way the behavior of the visual observer. In both cases, the total range over which one finds good differential discrimination at any given adaptation level is approximately two log units.

Curve (B) in Figure 9 shows what happens if we repeat the same experiment, but this time with the adaptation light two log units higher than for the experiment represented in Figure 9 (A). As you can see, the same thing happens as in the previous experiment. The firing rate for the eye completely adapted to the new adaptation level is again about 25 action potentials/second. And, again, brief increases and decreases in light intensity lead to sharp changes if they are not outside the range of about plus and minus one log unit from the adaptation level. The essential point of these experiments is that the single visual cell, much as the visual behavior of the viewer, shows good differential discrimination over a fairly restricted intensity range around any given adaptation level. The process that permits a change in the center point of this range is, of course, adaptation.

SPECTRAL SENSITIVITY
Thus far no mention has been made of the wavelength of the light as a factor influencing visual sensitivity. But it is an important

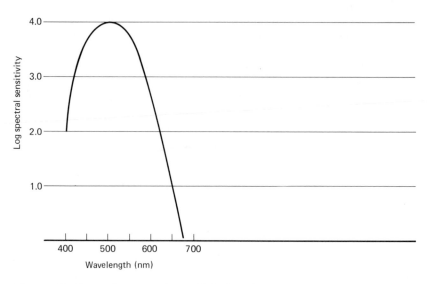

Figure 10. *Scotopic spectral sensitivity function.*

one, for if the threshold for seeing is measured in the dark-adapted eye, the intensity of the light needed to reach threshold varies for different wavelengths. Measurements of this kind yield a curve of the sort shown in Figure 10. This curve is called a *scotopic* (dim light) *spectral sensitivity function.* It shows that the dark-adapted eye is maximally sensitive to a light having a wavelength of about 500 nm and that sensitivity falls off toward both the short wavelengths (like 400 nm) and dramatically toward the long wavelengths (like 650 nm). Such functions have practical importance in specifying whether a light needs to be made more or less intense to have the same visual effect as a light of some other wavelength.

The scotopic spectral sensitivity function has precisely the same shape as the absorption curve for the photopigment found in the rods (rhodopsin). This correspondence means that vision under scotopic conditions is mediated solely by the operation of the rod photo-receptors.

If one repeats the basic experiment we have been describing, that of measuring a spectral sensitivity function, but this time does it with the eye adapted to a higher light level (like the light level at which you are now reading), a different spectral sensitivity function emerges. This type of function is called a *photopic* (bright light) *spectral sensitivity function.* As the photopic function drawn in Figure 11 shows, peak sensitivity under daylight conditions is at

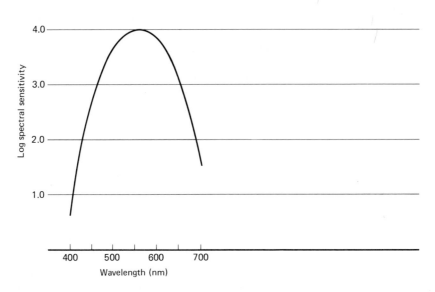

Figure 11. *Photopic spectral sensitivity function.*

about 550 nm, as compared to the peak at 500 nm seen under dim light conditions. The photopic sensitivity function has the same utility as the scotopic function—it permits one to adjust the intensity of lights having different wavelengths so they will be equally effective. However, the mechanisms underlying the photopic function are not as straightforward as those related to the scotopic function. It is known that the photopic spectral sensitivity function is based on the operation of cones and that primate cones contain three different types of photopigments. The photopic function represents the combined absorption characteristics of these pigments. However, the manner in which the absorption characteristics of these three pigments are combined to yield a single photopic function depends on several things, including the type of method used to measure the function. Here it is sufficient to know that the photopic spectral sensitivity function reflects the operation of cone receptors and the photopigments contained therein.

Earlier we saw in the dark-adaptation function evidence for the operation of two separate systems, the rods and cones. This observation was a special case showing the existence of scotopic and photopic systems. This dual-system arrangement that causes a change in the capacities of the visual system as one goes from dark adapted to light adapted is referred to as *visual duplicity.* The transition from scotopic to photopic vision as light level is increased is known as the *Purkinje shift* in honor of Johannes Purkinje, a Czech physician who in 1825 made the first systematic observations on this change. There is one other important difference between scotopic and photopic vision—vision at scotopic light levels is colorless; color appears at those light levels where the eye's spectral sensitivity function is that of Figure 11. In fact, it is said that Purkinje first became interested in the transition from photopic to scotopic vision when he noted that red and blue flowers which appeared equally bright under daylight conditions did not appear equally bright during the fading twilight. Under these latter conditions, the blue flowers now appeared brighter. Look again at figures 10 and 11 and assume that Purkinje's blue and red flowers reflected wavelengths of about 500 and 640 nm respectively. You should be able to discern the basis for his observation on brightness change.

SPATIAL SENSITIVITY

Our normal visual world consists of complex intermixtures of lights whose wavelengths and intensities vary from location-to-location in visual space. It could justifiably be argued that the central task of the visual system is to discriminate between inputs arriving from different spatial locations. As along other dimensions, our visual systems are exceptionally good at making spatial discriminations. Here we will consider a few of the features involved in man's ability to organize visual space.

There are many different ways to measure the acuteness of spatial vision. Likely the most familiar is that of a common acuity test where the individual is asked to tell whether the gap in a C-shaped figure is perceptible. The width of the gap is then varied so as to permit a threshold measurement. The threshold is usually expressed in angular terms with a gap separation of about one minute of arc frequently taken as "normal performance."[2] A gap of this size corresponds to a distance along the retina of about five microns. Under a wide variety of measurement conditions, spatial resolution can be shown to be much better than even this. For example, a telephone wire seen against a blue sky is still visible at substantial distances—indeed at distances where the image of the wire amounts to less than one second of arc.

Not surprisingly, many aspects of the measurement situation affect how well we are able to make spatial discriminations. Two are of primary importance, with one being obvious: the degree of spatial separation between the objects we are trying to discriminate. Consider the pair of black bars shown in Figure 12. A typical measurement might consist of determining at what point the subject sees two bars and at what point he sees only a single one. The manipulation is simply to move the two bars successively closer together until

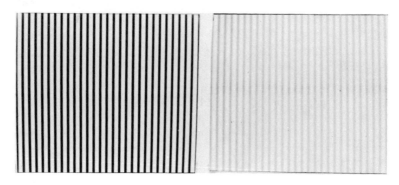

Figure 12. *The separation between the bars is the same for those on the left and those on the right, but those on the right have much lower contrast. If you move away from the picture, you will see that the high-contrast bars are much more discriminable than the low-contrast bars.*

they appear as one. The second factor influencing the ability to make this discrimination is the difference in intensity coming from the bars and from the background on which the bars are presented. Thus if the bar is made a gray rather than black, the minimal separation of bars that is discriminable increases. And the amount it increases depends on how closely the grays of the bars approach the appearance of the background. This second factor is called *contrast.* The effect on spatial resolution of decreasing contrast can be easily seen in Figure 12.

Since both contrast and spatial separation are determinants of spatial resolution, it makes sense to measure their effects jointly. Accordingly, one of the common modern methods used to measure spatial resolution involves determining the minimal contrast needed to reach threshold for any given degree of spatial separation. Typically, some sort of repeating test pattern is used, like a series of parallel bars. For a given spatial separation between bars, the contrast between the bars and the background is diminished until the subject is no longer able to see the bars. This same procedure is then repeated for a range of different degrees of bar separation. Measurements of this kind are illustrated in Figure 13 where threshold contrast is plotted against spatial frequency (spatial frequency, here given in cycles/degree, is the number of complete repetitions of the stimulus pattern per degree of visual angle and thus reflects the distance between the bars). For this measurement situation, the sensitivity of the eye is highest when spatial frequency is about 5 cycles/degree (this corresponds to a bar separation of about 6 minutes) and falls off when spatial frequency is higher and when it is lower than this. One important point here is that not only do we need higher contrast to resolve the higher spatial frequencies (that is,

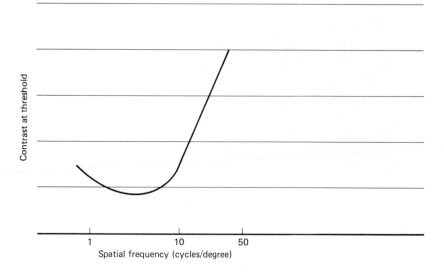

Figure 13. *This figure shows the amount of contrast necessary to resolve the structure in a repeating pattern of bars. The contrast required for resolution was measured at each of a variety of different bar separations (spatial frequencies). Note that higher contrast is required for both higher and lower frequencies than for some intermediate values.*

when the bars are close together), but we also need higher contrast to resolve the lower spatial frequencies (that is, when the bars are far apart).

How is it that we are able to distinguish between some spatial stimuli and not others? If you will recall for a moment the structure of the retina it will be clear that it is possible to think of the retina as a mosaic with the individual photoreceptors serving as the elements in this mosaic. It would be tempting to suppose that stimuli whose images fall on different elements could be discriminated from each other, those whose images fall on the same elements could not be discriminated. Unfortunately, this runs into some problems, not the least of which is that the outputs from a number of photoreceptors are fed into a single ganglion cell. If two different photoreceptors (through some intervening cells) activate a single ganglion cell, how can the effects of stimulating the two photoreceptors be kept separate? Perhaps one should think of the ganglion cells, not the photoreceptors, as the elements in the mosaic.

This latter idea is an attractive one for at least one reason. This is that the density of ganglion cells declines from the center of the fovea to the periphery of the retina. And so does our spatial resolution. In fact, as Figure 14 shows, visual acuity falls off precipitously for locations outside of the fovea.

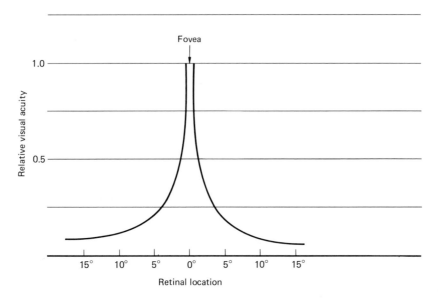

Figure 14. *Visual acuity for different retinal locations. The best visual acuity is given a value of 1.0. Thus at about 2–3° from the fovea, visual acuity is only about half as good as it is at the fovea.*

To discuss the possible roles of the ganglion cells, we need to add a little information about their functional properties. As we saw earlier, nerve cells in the visual system communicate information through increases and decreases in the rates of their electrical discharges. A good deal has been learned about the ways in which such single cells deal with spatial information. If you think for a moment about the organization of the retina, it should be clear that any single cell must receive input from only a restricted portion of visual space (this is true since no single cell receives input from all of the photoreceptors). The restricted portion of visual space that supplies input to a cell is called the cell's *receptive field.* To map a receptive field, the experimenter records the electrical activity of a single visual cell as various visual stimuli are presented to the eye, for example, spots of light in various locations in space. The result of such a procedure is a two dimensional map showing which locations in visual space the cell is "looking at" through all its peripheral connections.

The receptive fields of mammalian ganglion cells were first mapped in the early 1950s. Figure 15 shows such a map for the receptive field of a ganglion cell from a cat retina. The total circular area defines the limits of the cell's receptive field. In accord with the way in which we have just defined a receptive field, only stimuli that fall in this limited area can influence the transmission of visual in-

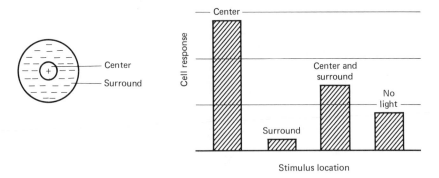

Figure 15. *The figure at the left shows a map for a typical ganglion cell receptive field. A plus means that the cell increases its firing rate when that region is illuminated. The graph at the right shows the response of this cell to various types of stimulation. Relative to "no light," the cell fires faster when the center region is illuminated and slower when the surround region is illuminated. When both the center and surround regions are illuminated simultaneously, the cell gives an intermediate response.*

formation by this cell. More importantly, the receptive field is divided into two concentric regions, a small center region and a larger sur-round region. The type of response given by the cell depends on which of these two regions receives light. If light falls only on the center, the rate of action potential discharge increases; if light falls on the surround region, the rate decreases. As pointed out before, either of these changes may be used to transmit visual information. How much of an increase (or decrease) one sees depends on the area and the intensity of the light falling on the center (or on the surround). If a stimulus falls on both the center and the surround, the response is intermediate to the response given to stimulation of either region alone. Thus the largest responses given by the cell are to stimuli that cover only one region.

Consider for a moment the response of the cell shown in Figure 15 to a bright circle on a dark background. If the bright circle is of the right size and if it is positioned so that it just covers the center of the receptive field, the cell will give a large increase in response. Now if the light in the center is made dimmer and the background is made brighter, the response gets smaller. In other words, the size of the response depends on the contrast between the two regions. Thus we see that contrast is an important determinant of single cell re-sponse just as it is for the visual behavior of its owner. What the cell reports (and thus transmits to other visual cells) is not just how much light falls in the receptive field, but how much light is falling on one spatial region of the receptive field *relative* to how much light is falling on other regions of the receptive field.

One other property of the ganglion cell receptive field is of interest. This is that the size of the center region varies drastically depending on where the ganglion cell is located in the retina. By this time you could probably correctly anticipate that those ganglion cells which receive input from receptors located in the fovea have small center regions and that the size of these center regions gets progressively larger as ganglion cells further and further from the fovea are examined. You will recall that measured visual acuity also declines progressively from the center to the periphery of the eye.

To summarize briefly, we have seen that the ability of the visual system to make spatial resolutions depends on the degree of spatial separation between the components of the visual stimulus and on the magnitude of contrast between these components. The kind of machinery needed to do this certainly must include some of the aspects of the ganglion cell receptive fields. These fields, by virtue of their variation in center size, will be very sensitive to the spatial separation of components in the visual stimulus. And by virtue of the antagonism between the center and surround regions in the receptive fields of these cells, these cells are also very sensitive to the contrast dimension.

VISUAL FORM AND THE CENTRAL VISUAL SYSTEM

As we have just seen, the receptive field characteristics of visual cells give an indication of the means by which various aspects of spatial stimuli are analyzed by the visual system. Thus it is not surprising that over the past 20 years considerable excitement has surrounded the experimental attempts to describe the receptive field characteristics of cells at many locations in the visual system. The reasoning behind such experiments is that if the receptive field characteristics of cells could be examined at each level in the visual system then it might be possible to see how a structured visual world is created from the showers of quanta continuously falling on the retinal surface.

Figure 16 is an attempt to summarize what a large number of visual scientists have learned about receptive field organization at various stations in the visual system. In each case the receptive field map gives an indication of which aspects of the visual stimulus are most important for the activation of the cell under investigation. Thus as Figure 16 shows, whereas the receptive fields of ganglion cells and cells in the lateral geniculate nucleus are circular and concentric in shape with a contrast interaction between the center and surround regions, the cells beyond this (at higher levels) have different receptive field characteristics. Specifically, cells in the visual cortex have

Location   Type of receptive field

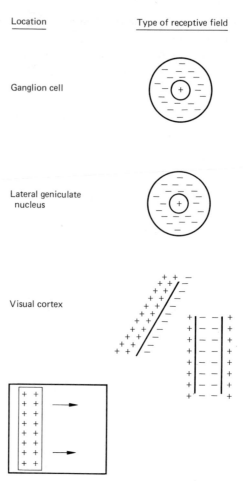

Ganglion cell

Lateral geniculate
nucleus

Visual cortex

Figure 16. *Types of receptive fields at various locations in the visual system. The properties of ganglion cells and cells in the lateral geniculate nucleus are those described for the cells in Figure 15. Three different cells are illustrated for locations in the visual cortex. The two on the upper right will respond best if only one region of their receptive fields is illuminated; that is, both will respond most vigorously to a light that has a plane surface, like a bar or an edge. The cell whose receptive field is illustrated at the lower left is more complicated. It responds best if a bar of light having the size indicated by the small rectangle (++) is moved from left to right within the area bounded by the larger rectangle.*

receptive fields organized along plane surfaces so that these cells are most vigorously activated if the visual stimulus contains a plane surface, and further, this plane surface must be appropriately positioned and oriented in visual space. As progressively higher levels in the visual cortex are examined, the receptive fields of cells become still more complex in the sense that the stimuli they will respond to

BOX 3

HOW TO BUILD, MAINTAIN, OR DESTROY
CORTICAL RECEPTIVE FIELDS

One of the most persistent issues in psychology deals with whether our abilities to perceive the visual world are given as a result of intrinsic brain organization or must be acquired through interactions with the environment. In short, are these capacities innate or acquired? Insofar as the receptive field organizations of cortical cells give an accurate indication of the processing of visual information, we have a means of approaching an answer to this question. For example, it is possible to ask if visually inexperienced animals have the same receptive field organizations as visually sophisticated animals. This very question was attacked experimentally by David Hubel and Torsten Wiesel about a decade ago (this work is summarized in D. H. Hubel, *The Physiologist,* 1967, *10,* 17–45). They found that the receptive fields of cells in the visual cortex of newborn kittens with no prior visual experience are similar in detail to those receptive fields found in adult cats. This suggested to them that the basic functional organization of the visual system is provided by innate (genetic) factors. However, they also found that if the kittens were deprived of normal visual experience during the first few weeks of life, the receptive fields became strikingly abnormal. These studies indicate that organization sufficient to provide for adult-type receptive fields is present at birth; but if the visual system is not used in the normal manner during early life, some profound degenerative changes occur. Although recent experiments have suggested that some modifications of the details of these early experiments may be required, in that some but perhaps not all features of receptive fields are present at birth, the basic approach is an important one in indicating the degree of interaction between genetic and experiential factors.

The Hubel-Wiesel experiments provided evidence for the occurrence of what is called a "critical period," a block of developmental time during which particular stimulus events need to be experienced to assure the viability of a sensory system. Still more recent experiments have explored the possibility that normal receptive field organization can be changed by rigorously controlling the animal's visual world during the critical period. This has been done, for example, by raising kittens in environments where they see only vertical stripes or only horizontal stripes. The results of these experiments constitute an impressive argument for functional plasticity during the critical period since animals raised viewing vertical stripes were later found to have a large majority of their cortical cells with receptive fields organized to detect vertical stripes while only a few cells were found to have receptive fields organized to detect anything else. Furthermore, these kittens behaved as though they were able to see only vertical stripes, appearing blind to other sorts of stimuli.

In sum, these experiments suggest that there is a substantial degree of innate organization in the visual system. If, however, the system is not activated appropriately it does not become organized into a fully normal visual system. Experiments being done in this area are not only uncovering important facts about brain organization, they are also providing some important practical implications inasmuch as many human sensory pathologies involve conditions where the normal inputs to the sensory system are either altered in quality or are completely excluded.

must be more precisely defined. For example, to activate some of these cells the experimenter must move (at a specific speed) a bar of light having the right orientation and size through the receptive field. Just how far this trend of increasing specificity goes is not clear since this work is anything but complete. Nevertheless, it is apparent that at least some cells have sophisticated receptive field organizations. For example, cells have been discovered in the monkey visual system (at a location beyond the visual cortex called the inferotemporal cortex) which responded only to the presentation of cardboard cutouts whose shapes were suspiciously similar to the outline of a monkey paw.

How do these indications of receptive field organization relate to our ability to discriminate visual form? We still do not know for sure. One theory is that the receptive fields indicate the ways in which various features of the visual stimulus are being analyzed—basic features like lines, angles, curvature, and so on. The notion is that a visual stimulus is detected by cells which are activated by virtue of a match between the receptive field characteristics of the cell and some feature of the stimulus. Thus a letter *A* can be discriminated from a letter *E* because various features of the two activate different sets of cells. Whether this possibility, or something entirely different, eventually turns out to be the correct explanation, it is already clear that the characterization of receptive fields of cells in the visual system is an important step toward understanding how the visual system is able to recreate spatial order in our visual worlds. See Box 3.

COLOR VISION

THE DEFINITION OF COLOR VISION

Why do some objects appear red, others green? How is it that some individuals are unable to tell apart red and brown fabrics which to you appear perfectly discriminable? Questions such as these have intrigued philosophers and scientists for many years. In this discussion, we will examine some aspects of the science of color vision.

As usual, we need to start with some definitions. The physical aspects of light critical for a discussion of color vision are wavelength, intensity, and *spectral purity.* Wavelength and intensity are already familiar to you. The *purity of a light* is defined as the degree to which the light is composed of a narrow band of wavelengths relative to the degree to which it is composed of achromatic light (an *achromatic light* is one in which all spectral wavelengths are represented—white light is the familiar example). Thus a light composed solely of wavelengths between 550 and 555 nm has very high purity.

Correlated with these three physical dimensions are three response dimensions (sometimes called psychological dimensions). Thus variations in intensity lead, primarily, to changes in perceived *brightness;* changes in wavelength are primarily correlated with changes in perceived *hue;* changes in purity are primarily correlated with changes in perceived *saturation.* The saturation dimension may be the most obscure. You can think of it as the degree to which a light is colored—a narrow band of wavelengths taken from the 625–650 nm portion of the spectrum appears as a highly saturated red. If some white light is added to this stimulus, it now appears pink; it has been desaturated.

The definition of the presence of color vision is straightforward, although sometimes the actual demonstration is not. An individual is said to possess color vision if that individual can discriminate between two stimuli having different wavelength compositions when factors other than the difference in wavelength are not available as cues for the discrimination. For example, we might test a subject to see if color vision is present by requiring him to discriminate between 500 and 600 nm. To eliminate all nonwavelength-related cues, we would have to be sure that the shapes of the two stimuli were the same, that one was not moving while the other was stationary, and so on. Perhaps most important, we would have to be careful that one light was not brighter than the other because a brightness difference can serve as a powerful cue that might permit an individual without color vision to make the discrimination correctly.

With few exceptions all humans succeed in the task just described. That is, the *presence* of some degree of color vision is virtually universal in our species. Not quite as many, but still almost all, will also succeed at a second, similar task: discriminating spectral stimuli from equally bright white ones. Some individuals (about 2–3 percent of European and North American populations) fail this discrimination for some particular wavelengths. Those who pass this test for all wavelengths are said to have *trichromatic* vision. Later on we will return to the interesting question of variation in color vision capacity.

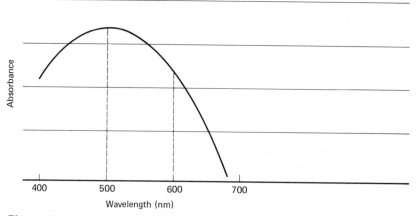

Figure 17. *Illustration of a color-vision test performed on a visual system based on a single type of photopigment. The locations of the two stimulus wavelengths are indicated by the dashed lines.*

MECHANISMS FOR COLOR VISION

All vision depends on the absorption of light by photopigments. Accordingly, it is reasonable to ask how these photopigments might contribute to color vision. You will recall that the efficiency of absorption of light by any photopigment depends on the wavelength of the light—some wavelengths are more likely to cause a photopigment change than others. Consider a visual system with a single type of photopigment of the sort shown in Figure 17. Further, suppose that this visual system is placed in a color vision test such that two stimuli having wavelengths of 500 and 600 nm are to be discriminated from each other. Since this photopigment is more sensitive to 500 nm than to 600 nm, if the two lights are of equal intensity, the 500 nm light will bleach greater amounts of the photopigment and hence cause a greater visual effect—that is, the 500 nm light will appear brighter. However, to demonstrate color vision, all cues other than the difference in wavelength must be irrelevant. If we simply increase the intensity of the 600 nm light, a point will be reached where its effect on the photopigment will be identical to the effect of the 500 nm light. In other words, a visual system based on a single photopigment is incapable of providing the information needed to produce color vision.

What if the visual system contains two different types of photopigments? Is that sufficient to provide for color vision? Figure 18 shows such a situation. Again imagine the lights to be discriminated are 500 and 600 nm. Note that each of these wavelengths will have an effect on both photopigments (*A* and *B*). Also note that the ratio of the effects on the two photopigments is different independent of the actual intensities of the two lights. That is, the 500 nm light always

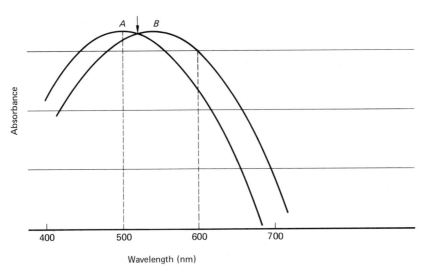

Absorbance

400   500   600   700

Wavelength (nm)

Figure 18. *Illustration of a color vision test performed on a visual system based on two photopigments (A & B). The locations of the two stimulus wavelengths are indicated by the dashed lines.*

has a greater effect on *A* than on *B*, while the reverse holds for the 600 nm light. A two-pigment system such as this is clearly capable of providing the information necessary to produce color vision. However, this system is not sufficient to produce normal color vision. Is it clear why this is so? It is because a light whose wavelength is at the location indicated by the small arrow affects both pigments equally. A stimulus containing all spectral wavelengths (a white) will also affect both systems equally. Thus although a two-pigment system will suffice to produce color vision, it is not sufficient to produce trichromatic vision.

With a system based on three photopigments all the requirements of normal color vision can be satisfied. As in the two-pigment system, the ratio differences are sufficient to always yield a different effect for any pair of stimulus wavelengths. And with three photopigments, there is no single spectral location where a wavelength will equally affect all three photopigments as in the two-photopigment case. Consequently, three photopigments are the minimal number required for normal human color vision.

Since color vision occurs under conditions where the cones are operative, it is not surprising that there is a long history of efforts to measure the characteristics of the photopigments in these receptors, but it has only been recently that some accurate indications of the cone photopigments have emerged. Figure 19 shows the approximate absorbance curves for these pigments. As predicted from argu-

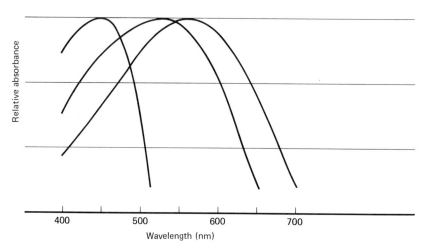

Figure 19. *The absorption curves for the three types of photopigment found in human-cone receptors.*

ments of the sort given above, there are three different classes of photopigments. The locations of the peaks of these photopigments are about 455, 535, and 570 nm. All color vision arises as a result of activation of these three pigments.

It has also now become clear in a general way how the nervous system analyzes color information. The essential key is that the outputs from a pair of cone pigments are subtracted from one another. This notion is easier to illustrate than it is to explain in words. Figure 20 attempts to do just this. There you will see how the outputs from a class of receptors containing a 535 nm peak photopigment are put together with the outputs from receptors containing a 570 nm photopigment. Activation of the 570 nm pigment causes the cell illustrated to increase its firing rate while activation of the 535 nm pigment causes the cell to decrease its firing rate. In effect, the cell algebraically adds up its inputs so that the amount it fires faster or slower depends on the relative activation of the two photopigments providing the cell's input.

Figure 20 shows only one of several such combinations formed by subtracting the output of one photopigment from that of another. Cells having such antagonistic inputs are called *chromatic-opponent cells*, and it is these cells which transmit the neural information necessary for color vision. These cells have been shown to relate to color vision in several ways. One way can be seen in Figure 20;

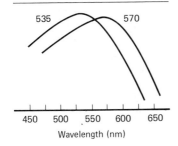
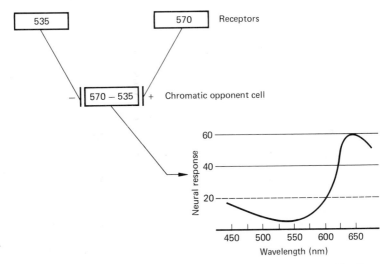

Figure 20. *Schematic showing of how color information is processed by the visual system. The receptors contain two types of photopigments (top graph). The signals from these two types of photopigments converge on a chromatic opponent cell. This cell discharges faster when it receives input from the 570 nm pigment and slower when it receives input from the 535 nm pigment. Thus how it responds depends on the amount it is activated by the 570 nm pigment, minus the amount it is activated by the 535 nm pigment. The bottom graph shows the rate of discharge for many different stimulus wavelengths relative to the discharge rate when no light falls on the eye.*

a cell of this kind is called a red-green cell because those parts of the spectrum that cause the cell to increase its firing rate are those that appear "red"; those parts of the spectrum that cause the cell to decrease its firing rate appear "green." Thus there seems to be a direct relationship between the activation of these cells and the color appearance of a stimulus.

Obviously, there is a good deal more to understanding the mechanisms of color vision than just the absorption characteristics of the cone photopigments and the response properties of the chromatic-opponent cells. For example, both the spatial and temporal

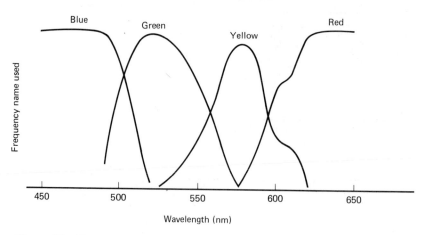

Figure 21. *The appearance of different spectral lights as judged by the use of color names by a normal human trichromat.*

features of a stimulus greatly determine its color appearance. Unfortunately, a clear understanding of how these aspects are dealt with by the visual system has still not been reached.

SOME ASPECTS OF NORMAL COLOR VISION

It was suggested previously that the color appearance of a stimulus may be correlated with a particular pattern of neural activity in some cells in the visual system. But are color appearances sufficiently the same for different individuals to support the notion of such a correlation? There is certainly no doubt that the richness of color vocabulary varies widely from person-to-person; a color you might call "yellow" might be called "ocher" by a painter. But does this imply that the appearances of colors are determined by training? Are, in fact, the appearances of spectral stimuli subject to scientific study?

Some answers to these questions come from experiments in which the naming of various colors is investigated. Such experiments suggest that, within a given culture, there is considerable uniformity and precision in the use of common color names. Figure 21 illustrates the results of an experiment in which a subject was required to name the colors of the spectral wavelengths. This subject was permitted to use only four names—blue, green, yellow, and red, although compounds of these were also permitted (yellow-red, blue-green, and so on). In the figure, the frequency of the particular color name used is plotted for various stimulus wavelengths. Other subjects give similar results. The point is that under these restricted conditions, the color names are applied uniformly by different individuals.

Beyond merely showing that the appearance of colors, at least as judged by the adequacy of naming, is similar across individuals,

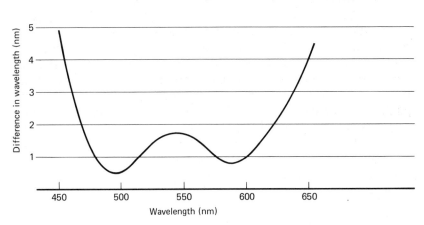

Figure 22. *Measurement of the ability of a human to discriminate between neighboring wavelengths. At each wavelength, the wavelength was changed until the subject could just detect a difference. The amount of difference required is plotted on the vertical axis.*

the color naming results shown in Figure 21 also indicate some aspects of color vision capacity. Note, for example, those parts of the spectrum where small changes in stimulus wavelengths lead to distinct changes in the color name applied. One such location is around 580 nm. This wavelength is called yellow; but at slightly longer wavelengths, the spectrum begins to appear reddish; while at slightly shorter wavelengths, the spectrum begins to appear greenish. On the other hand, there are locations (for example, "blue") where the same name is applied over large wavelength ranges. These results suggest that the sensitivity to wavelength differences varies across the spectrum.

Figure 22 indicates that this supposition is indeed true. This figure summarizes the results from an experiment where the subject was required to discriminate between neighboring wavelengths. The results plotted show how much wavelength had to be changed for the subject to tell they were different. As you can see, sensitivity to wavelength change is very great at about 580 and 500 nm, just where Figure 21 shows that the appearance of the spectrum is changing rapidly.

The other feature worthy of note in Figure 22 is just how acute human color vision is. At the most favorable locations in the spectrum differences in wavelength of less than 1 nm can be discriminated. We concluded from measurements of how little light the visual system can detect that the visual system is enormously good at its tasks—clearly our color vision abilities reinforce this conclusion.

VARIATION IN COLOR VISION

In 1798, the famous chemist Dalton reported that his own color vision was different from that of most others. In particular, he noted that all spectral lights appeared to him as either purple, blue, or yellow. Although this was not the first recorded indication of the fact that there are important individual differences in color vision, it did greatly stimulate the scientific study of those people who are commonly called color-blind. Actually, "color blind" is a very inaccurate term—as indicated previously, only a few individuals fail the defining test for color vision and are therefore truly color blind. For the vast majority of cases, the term *defective color vision* is much more appropriate if you understand that phrase to identify those individuals whose color vision varies in specific ways from the color vision of most of our species.

Defective color vision may occur either as an inherited condition or be acquired as a result of some pathological state. Almost all we know of defective color vision concerns the inherited forms. Those very rare individuals who fail the defining test for color vision, who are truly color blind, are called *monochromats.* For them the world consists solely of blacks, whites, and shades of gray. Most color-defective observers do have some color vision. As we noted previously, individuals able to discriminate all spectral lights from equally bright white lights are called trichromats. This is the norm for human color vision. However, some people are able to pass this test, but still turn out to be different from most individuals. These are called *anomalous trichromats.* The nature of these anomalies can be seen in the following way. If an individual with color vision is required to mix together (by superimposing them on the same area of the visual field) a red light and a green light to match in appearance a yellow light, almost all will use very close to the same proportions of red and green light in the mixture. But some people will require much more red light than the normal while others will require much more green light than the normal. The former are classified as *protanomalous* trichromats, the latter as *deuteranomalous* trichromats. There is also a third, extremely rare, type of anomalous color vision called *tritanomalous* color vision.

A more severe color vision defect is seen in those individuals who fail the test for normal vision in that there are some specific wavelengths they are unable to discriminate from equally bright white lights. These people are classified as having *dichromatic* color vision. Depending on which particular wavelengths they are unable to discriminate from white, they have either *protanopic, deuteranopic,* or *tritanopic* color vision. The color vision of the dichromats is much like that expected from the system based on two photopigments shown in Figure 18. It should be noted that there are many ways other than

TABLE 2.1 HUMAN DEFECTIVE COLOR VISION

CLASSIFICATION	APPROXIMATE PERCENTAGE OF POPULATION
Anomalous trichromats	
Protanomalous	1.0
Deuteranomalous	4.6
Tritanomalous	exceedingly rare
Dichromats	
Protanopes	1.2
Deuteranopes	1.4
Tritanopes	.008–.0015
Monochromats	
Several varieties	.003

Source: H. Davson, ed. *The Eye.* New York: Academic Press, 1962, p. 282.

those listed here to diagnose the various types of color defective vision. Table 2.1 summarizes all of these various types of defective color vision and lists the appropriate percentages of the population in each category.

That many of the types of defective color vision are inherited has been known for about a hundred years. The gene for defective color vision is localized on one of the sex chromosomes (the X chromosome). Since the gene is a recessive one and since males carry only one X chromosome, defective color vision of the inherited variety is much more common among males than among females. In fact, only about 0.4 percent of all females have defective color vision, while about 8 percent of all males show the defect.

In addition to the enormous difference in incidence between the two sexes, there is also a striking difference in the incidence of defective color vision associated with both geographical and racial differences. The 8 percent figure given above is for white males. Nonwhite races show considerably lower frequencies; for example, Japanese and Chinese males have an incidence of defective color vision between 4 and 6 percent. The lowest incidence known is among American Indians. The figure for males of this group is about 2.5 percent.

It is intriguing to consider that the colors experienced by those having defective color vision are different from those of the normal. But how different? It is not easy to tell because the color vocabularies of the color defective are much the same as normal. It is easy to see why this is so since everyone grows up learning that sky is blue, grass is green, and so on. The point is that there are many cues other than color that permit the conventional use of color names. Indeed, many people are surprised to find that they have defective color vision when they are finally appropriately tested. There is one instance that gives some insight into the color experiences of dichromats. It comes from the fact that very, very rarely an individual will be discovered who has normal color vision in one eye and defective color vision in the other eye. Studies of several people who had one dichromatic, one trichromatic eye suggest that the dichromat (at least the protanope and the deuteranope) perceives all colors as being either of two hues, blue or yellow. These findings fit well with the earlier astute observations of Dalton (himself a dichromat) mentioned above.

What is different about the visual systems of those people showing defective color vision? This question, despite a lot of attention, cannot be fully and certainly answered. In some cases the reason for the defect is clear. Thus the dichromatic protanope is so because there are only two classes of cone photopigments in his eye—the pigment having peak absorption at 570 nm is missing. In other cases, the reason for the defect is more obscure. In addition to the possibility that one of the photopigments is simply not present, there are a variety of other situations that would also lead to non-normal color vision. For example, one of the three types of cone photopigments might be present in abnormal quantity or the absorption curve for one of the three might be altered in some way. The basis of the defect need not lie in photopigment alterations—there might be some changes in the visual pathways (for example, some of the neural junctions needed to produce chromatic-opponent cells might not be formed). The point is that there are a variety of ways in which failure in the visual system might result in defective color vision. Some of these are well known; others still remain to be established.

One final point about defective color vision. We tend to think of those having defective color vision as forming a separate group. However, everyone has defective color vision under some circumstances. Thus we are all monochromats at scotopic light levels. Furthermore, the normal trichromasy which most of us experience is only a property of the central portion of the retina. If stimuli are imaged onto the peripheral portion of the retina, the resulting color vision is drastically changed from normal trichromasy. Indeed, it is possible to arrange the stimulus circumstances appropriately to mimic any of the various types of defective color vision in the "normal" visual system. Some experiments have been directed toward characterizing color vision in nonhuman species. The results of these endeavors are summarized in Box 4.

BOX 4

PHYLOGENY OF COLOR VISION

Color vision is not a universal attribute of the species inhabiting this planet. Indeed, substantial variation occurs in the degree to which various species have been found to possess this capacity. Determining whether a particular species has color vision is a task requiring both care and patience. Thus as yet, only a small fraction of the total number of living species have been adequately tested. Listed here are some representative groups in which some information about color vision capacity is available.

Insects. Many insects are known to have color vision, with that of the honeybee having been most extensively studied. The bee has been shown to be sensitive to wavelengths in the range from 300 to 650 mm and thus sees wavelengths from the ultraviolet portion of the spectrum which to us are invisible.

Invertebrates. Only a small number of invertebrate species have been investigated. Of these, some species of spiders apparently have color vision. There have also been several experiments on color vision in the octopus. Unfortunately, the results of these studies are equivocal; and it is still not clear whether these creatures have color vision.

Vertebrates. Among the vertebrates, wide variation occurs in the presence and type of color vision.

1. Fish—Some fish species are known to have good color vision. For example, the goldfish has trichromatic color vision. Surprisingly, little scientific attention has been paid to those game fish commonly pursued with lures and flies of gaudy hue.
2. Amphibians—Color vision has been demonstrated in several amphibian species. Some species of frogs are claimed to have trichromatic vision.
3. Birds—A majority of the species of birds examined appear to have good color vision. The mechanism for color vision in most birds is somewhat different from that of man in that there are colored oil droplets in the retina through which the light must pass to reach the photopigments. The presence of these oil droplets provides the possibility for the elaboration of color vision in a retina containing only a single type of photopigment with multiple kinds of oil droplets.
4. Rodents—There is wide variation in visual capacity among the rodents. Some (like rats and mice) have heavily rod-dominated retinas and little or no color vision. Others (some members of the squirrel family) have heavily cone-dominated retinas and color vision. The color vision of some of the types of ground squirrels is dichromatic, greatly similar to that of the human protanope.
5. Felines—Because the domestic cat is a favorite subject for study by visual physiologists, it has received special attention. Although it was once believed that the cat was color-blind, it

is now clear that the cat does have color vision in the definitional sense. However, the difficulty in demonstrating this capacity suggests that it is not an important feature of the visual world of the cat. Such as it is, the cat's color vision is probably dichromatic in nature.

6. Primates—Good color vision is widespread among the nonhuman primates. The color vision of the Old World monkeys and the Great Apes is apparently similar to the normal trichromatic vision of humans. Some of the South American monkeys have color vision similar to that of human anomalous trichromats. A few species of primitive monkeys are predominantly nocturnal on habit. Although none of these has been studied carefully, color vision in them is likely to be absent entirely or rudimentary at best.

FINAL CONSIDERATIONS

Thus far we have discussed the structure of the visual system, some aspects of visual sensitivity, and color vision. Depending on how successful this discussion has been, you may be either depressed or exhilarated to learn that these topics are representative of only a small fraction of what is known about vision and the visual system. The visual system we have been considering so far is a highly artificial one in the sense that it has only one eye, that neither the eye nor the visual world moves, and that it is a visual world in which the stimuli are mostly brief flashes of light. Here some features that bridge the gap between this highly artificial situation and the complex world of real vision will be briefly mentioned.

BINOCULAR VISION

Binocular vision is the vision resulting from the use of two eyes; *monocular vision* results from the use of one eye. Obviously, to have binocular vision one must have a visual system in which the two eyes point at the same locations in space. In some species the possibilities for binocular vision are minimal; for example, in animals like the rat, the eyes are located on the sides of a triangle-shaped head and thus point in almost opposite directions. However, in many mammals the eyes are located such that the two point in more or less the same directions and consequently provide the possibility for binocular vision. Figure 23 shows the extent of the monocular and binocular visual fields for some representative species.

What advantages accrue to those animals having binocular as opposed to monocular vision? At first glance it looks as if it would be much more useful to have the eyes point in different directions. Thus the squirrel whose visual fields are schematized in Figure 23 is able, by

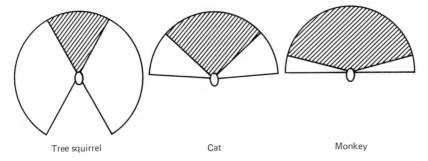

Figure 23. *The extent of the visual field in three kinds of animals. The small circle represents the position of the head. In each case, the limits of the visual field (with the head pointed toward the top of the page) is given by the large circle. The striped portion shows the region of binocular vision; the unstriped portion shows the region of monocular vision.*

virtue of its laterally located eyes, to simultaneously view a much larger portion of the world than is the monkey whose frontally located eyes restrict the total visual field to about 180°. The great advantage associated with binocular vision, and presumably the reason for the evolutionary migration of eyes to the front of the head so that they receive a common view, turns out to be the manner in which binocular vision aids in the localization of objects in space.

The pupils of the two eyes of man are separated by about six or seven centimeters. Consequently, the two eyes provide slightly different views of the world. If you view an object held at arms length and alternately close the two eyes you will easily be able to appreciate the degree of difference in views that the two eyes have. And by moving the object you can see how the degree of difference in view for the two eyes depends on how far away the object is: if it is close, the differences in view for the two eyes are much greater than if the object is distant. Since the degree to which the views of the two eyes differ depends on the distance of the object from the eyes, the degree of difference might provide a powerful clue about the distance from the observer to the object he is looking at.

The degree to which the two eyes receive different views of an object can be objectively measured. This difference, specified in degrees of angle, is called *retinal disparity*. A sensation of visual depth can be artificially created by providing disparity between the views seen by the two eyes. This fact is the basis of what are called *stereoscopic depth* effects. In the early 1800s Charles Wheatstone showed that if a pair of two-dimensional views of the same scene (but taken as from a pair of cameras separated by about the distance between the two eyes) are presented separately to the two eyes, then the result is the appearance of a single unified scene possessing substantial depth. Variations on this scheme have been used many times since then to produce the appearance of three dimensional depth in a two dimensional medium—as in the 3D movies that enjoyed brief popularity several years ago.

To summarize, binocular vision consists of the unification of two slightly different views of the world. It arises by virtue of the physical separation between the two eyes. The degree of difference in view, the retinal disparity, serves as an indication of the distance from the viewer to the viewed object. It should not however be concluded that retinal disparity is the only mechanism used in the judgment of distance. Indeed, there are many others whose interrelationships are not yet fully explored. For example, the degree of lens accommodation depends on the distance of a viewed object, and this information may be used to aid in the judgment of distance. In addition, the positioning of the two eyes relative to one another changes (converges and diverges) depending on the distance of the eyes from the object and this also can serve as an indication of distance. Finally, there are also a variety of so-called secondary cues to distance. The major reason for emphasizing retinal disparity more than the other mechanisms is because some information now exists on the processing of disparity information by the central visual system, a topic to be considered now.

At all locations prior to the visual cortex, the visual system is monocular—that is, a given cell is influenced by light entering through one eye only. Cells in the visual cortex (and beyond) are binocular in the sense that they are influenced by stimulation of either eye or by stimulation of both eyes simultaneously. As described previously, the receptive field characteristics of cortical cells have been studied rather extensively. Nothing was said about how the presence of input from both eyes influences the receptive field organization. In the cat, the species most extensively studied, it has been found that a receptive field can be mapped with first one eye covered then the other. The characteristics of the receptive fields mapped in this way are much the same for either eye. That is, if the cell requires a stimulus moving toward the left when the right eye is stimulated, it also requires a stimulus moving toward the left when the left eye is stimulated. However, the positioning of the receptive fields is slightly different for tests through the two eyes. Figure 24 shows receptive field maps for two such cells. The essential point is that the location the cell is "looking at" through one eye is slightly different from the location viewed through the other eye. This is to say, some degree of retinal disparity must be present for a stimulus to fall cleanly in both receptive fields at the same time. Thus in addition to the right location in visual space, the right orientation, the right movement, and so on, the cell also requires a particular retinal disparity before it is maximally

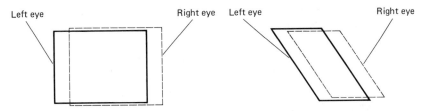

Figure 24. *Receptive fields for two binocular neurons. In each case, the lines show the limits of the receptive field when the receptive field was mapped through the left eye (solid line) and through the right eye (dashed line). Note that to maximally activate the cell with both eyes open, the stimulus must be such as to lead to some degree of retinal disparity.*

activated. Since a given retinal disparity corresponds to a given distance between the stimulus and the observer, these cells *could* be transmitting information about distance as well as information about stimulus form and location.

EYE MOVEMENTS

Without being too obtrusive, try watching the eyes of someone engaged in a conversation with a couple of acquaintances. You will be impressed to note that the eyes are in almost continuous movement giving a striking display of mobility and coordination. The major reason for all this activity is not difficult to discern. It is because only the very central portion of the retina possesses the high spatial acuity required for a large majority of common visual tasks. Consequently, the eyes must move to line up continuously the central part of the retina with that location in the world of current interest.

Movements of the eye are produced by the operation of the *extraocular muscles.* There are twelve of these muscles, six attached to the globe of each eye. The control of eye position produced by the contractions and relaxations of these muscles in various combinations is both rapid and precise. The muscles themselves are under the control of a complicated network of cells in the brain. The result of the operation of the extraocular muscles is to produce eye movements. These movements are binocularly coordinated; that is, the two eyes move together. The reason for this coordination is to insure that the image of a viewed object falls on corresponding regions of the two retinas. If the image does not fall on corresponding regions, double vision (*diplopia*) results. There are a large number of conditions that may result in the disruption of this coordination. For example, inebriating doses of alcohol often lead to diplopia.

Visual scientists have found it necessary to distinguish several kinds of eye movements. Briefly, these are (1) *Saccadic eye movements*—these move the eyes very rapidly to shift the gaze from one location to another. The return of the eyes of a reader from the right margin to the left margin of a page is a familiar example of such movement. (2) *Smooth pursuit eye movements*—eye movements of this sort are made in tracking a moving target, as in following the flight of a ball through the air. Although this may appear simple, the coordination required to match the velocity of the eye movement to the velocity of a moving target is an impressive neurological feat. (3) *Reflex eye movements*—these eye movements are used to compensate for the movements of the head and body; for example, raising the head results in a lowering of the eyes. The goal of such eye movement is to help maintain a stable visual world in the face of continuous movements of the head and body. (3) *Vergence eye movements*—the eye movements here involve moving the eyes in opposite directions. If you fixate a pencil and move it toward your face the eyes will point inward (convergence); when you move the pencil back away from your face the eyes will point outward again (divergence).

In addition to these four types of movement there is another kind of eye movement of interest. These are the very small eye movements that occur continuously. In fact, these movements are present even when you try to stare as fixedly as you can at some object. The result of such movement is that the image of an object, even a fixated one, is continuously moved around over a small area of the retina. About 20 years ago the striking discovery was made that when these eye movements are artificially eliminated, the subject's view of the world begins to fade almost immediately; and eventually, all the subject perceives is a structureless world often described as being like a dense gray fog. This result is surprising since one might have thought that the elimination of these small eye movements would result in even better spatial vision than one normally has. Apparently, the visual system is designed such that it needs continuous change to operate normally. These small eye movements seem to provide such change in those situations where no external change may be present.

MOVING EYES, MOVING WORLD

Consider two situations. In one a bar-shaped stimulus is moved from left to right across the visual field. In the other, the bar is held stationary while the eyes are moved smoothly from left to right across the visual field. In each case the retina receives light in the same way —an image of the bar crosses the retinal surface. However, in the first case the bar is seen as moving while in the second case the bar is seen as stationary. This illustration points out that there is considerably more to vision than can be understood by knowing the distribution of quanta reaching the retina. Indeed, in all but the very simplest situations a complete explanation of vision will have to include an understanding of the origins and interactions of many signals—some from the retina, some from other sensory systems, some from brain locations that contain information about past experiences.

It would be nice if it were possible to end this discussion by reporting how the visual system differentiates the two types of movement information. Although there is no lack of speculation on this issue, no firm facts exist. One popular theory is that movement of the eyes produces a signal which is then compared at some location in the visual system to the signal produced by activation of the retina. If the two signals are the same (that is, if the signaled amount of eye movement corresponds to the amount the stimulus moved across the retina) they cancel each other with the result that the visual stimulus is seen as stationary. If the two are not the same, the stimulus is seen as moving. Unfortunately, there is no convincing evidence for this scheme or for any of the alternatives that have been proposed to solve the problem of how we are able to discriminate these two movement situations. In a way this issue characterizes much of the study of vision, for, although we have learned much and are at least cognizant of most of the problems, our understanding is still incomplete. This is fortunate for those who enjoy studying vision and puzzling over the visual system. None of this group expects to be unemployed in the near future.

NOTES

1. Because the intensity ranges typically used to specify visual capacity are very large, it is customary to use logarithmic scales. Thus the total range of functional vision referred to above is 10 log units.

2. You are undoubtedly familiar with the term "20/20," often used to report visual acuity as measured in clinical tests. In this designation, the first number refers to the testing distance in feet. The second number gives a calculation of the distance at which the "average eye" discriminates what the tested eye discriminates at 20 feet. Thus if the second number is larger than 20, your acuity is poorer than this arbitrary average. If it exceeds it by any appreciable amount, supplementary lenses are usually prescribed.

SUGGESTED READINGS

Begbie, G. H. *Seeing and the eye.* Garden City, New York: Anchor Books, 1973.

Gregory, R. L. *Eye and brain.* 2d Ed. New York: McGraw-Hill, 1973.
> These two books contain treatments of various aspects of vision. Both are written at about the same level as this unit. The Begbie book emphasizes the basic aspects of vision, while the Gregory book covers a variety of issues in visual perception.

Tansley, K. *Vision in vertebrates.* London: Chapman & Hall, 1965.
> Although now somewhat out of date, this small book has a good treatment of the comparative aspects of vision.

Cornsweet, T. N. *Visual perception.* New York: Academic Press, 1970.
> This is a superb book covering the basic features of vision. It is more rigorous than anything else listed here, but well worth the effort for the interested student.

The following list contains references to articles that have appeared in the monthly magazine *Scientific American.* Each article is written by a specialist in the topic area. The articles are profusely illustrated; and although they vary in difficulty, most are easy to comprehend.

Pritchard, R. M. Stabilized images on the retina. June 1961.

Rushton, W. A. H. Visual pigments in man. November 1962.

Hubel, D. H. The visual cortex of the brain. November 1963.

MacNichol, E. F., Jr. Three-pigment color vision. December 1964.

Fender, D. H. Control mechanisms of the eye. July 1964.

Michael, C. R. Retinal processing of visual images. May 1969.

Ratliff, F. Contour and contrast. June 1972.

Pettigrew, J. D. The neurophysiology of binocular vision. August 1972.

Werblin, F. S. The control of sensitivity in the retina. January 1973.

Rushton, W. A. H. Visual pigments and color blindness. March 1975.

Johansson, G. Visual motion perception. June 1975.

HEARING
UNIT THREE

CHARLES S. WATSON
Boys Town Institute for Communication
Disorders in Children, Omaha

INTRODUCTION TO HEARING

Sometimes the newcomer is surprised to learn that psychologists have been among the most active investigators of human hearing. A little reflection on the importance of the spoken word to the intellectual and social development of man may make this seem less strange.

Modern psychological science grew from a combination of laboratory-based physiology and objective philosophy, which merged into *experimental psychology* in the 1860s. The first great student of this new subject, Herman von Helmholtz, was actually trained as a physician and thought of himself as a physiologist and physicist rather than a psychologist. But many of his ideas were psychological and are an excellent starting point for our discussion.

Helmholtz stressed two basic principles in his work on the human senses. One of these was that to understand sensory activity the scientist must learn the nature of the physical stimulus and how this stimulus is processed by the sensory systems. The other was that the human observer normally perceives his world quite well without knowledge of either the nature of the cues (physical stimuli) on which his perception depends or the ways those cues interact with his sensory nervous system. To see what Helmholtz meant by the second principle, try the following simple experiment. Have a couple of your friends stand about five feet in front of you and about one foot to either side of your "median plane" (the imaginary plane surface that can be passed, front to back, through your head and which divides it in its two most symmetrical halves). They should now hold their hands toward you to form a row of four hands with about one foot between each pair. Now shut your eyes, have one of your friends snap the fingers of one hand, and see whether you can decide which hand was the culprit. After a few practice trials most people can pick the correct hand without error. What aspect of the sounds are you using to arrive at your decision? How is this information extracted by your ears and the rest of your auditory apparatus? Unless you have read or been told about the auditory localization of sounds, you probably cannot answer these questions. But whether you know how you do it has little or no bearing on your ability to notice where sounds seem to be coming from. You process certain subtle cues and arrive at your final conclusion without knowing how you did it. Helmholtz called this process *unconscious inference,* by which he not only

Note: The thoughtful criticisms of Margo W. Skinner, Henry W. Wroton and Walt Jesteadt contributed significantly to this unit. Wroton also designed and drafted the original artwork and coped with many difficulties encountered on the way to a final draft. Preparation of the manuscript was supported by Program Project Grant NS03856 from the National Institute of Neurological and Communicative Disorders and Stroke to the Central Institute for the Deaf, St. Louis, Missouri, and by the Boys Town Institute for Communication Disorders in Children, Omaha, Nebraska.

meant that you perceive without knowing what the immediate stimuli are, but also that you generally are unaware of the degree to which the way you hear or see depends on past experience. To get a hint about how your ears allow you to localize sounds, repeat the demonstration, but this time with one ear plugged.

In brief, auditory perception, like any other sensory information processing, depends on the physical stimulus, how that stimulus affects the nervous system, and on our past experience with various sounds.

THE DOMAIN OF SOUND

A sound or an *acoustic event* consists of a series of high- and low-pressure regions that move or are *propagated* through a gaseous, fluid, or solid conducting medium. Imagine a small board that is moved quickly over a distance of a few inches in a pond, forcing a wave ahead of it. When the board is stopped the wave continues for quite a way, getting smaller and smaller until it is "damped out." Now if this little wave reaches a toy boat as it moves along, what happens to that boat? It moves up and down, but is not carried along with the wave because the water around it moves up and down, but not laterally. Similarly, in the case of airborne sound waves, consisting of condensations and rarefactions of gas, individual molecules do not move from a talker to a listener. Instead one molecule agitates its immediate neighbor, which in turn passes on that effect, until the original energy is used up by heating the atmosphere. (All speakers are thus basically producers of hot air.) The intensity of the sound is measured by the amount of change in pressure from peak to valley as shown in Figure 1A. Sound waves are propogated through air at about 1130 feet per second. They lose *amplitude* (peak-to-valley distance) in accordance with the *inverse square law*. That is, the intensity of a sound coming will be reduced by a factor of 4 when you double your distance from it and by a factor of 25 when you move 5 times as far away. The inverse square law describes the loss of sound intensity as distance from the source increases whether the sound is transmitted through air, water, or a solid body. But sound passing through water goes about 5 times as fast as sound in air, about a mile in 1 second. Sound passes through a steel bar about 15 times as fast as through air. As the tuning fork in Figure 1A moves back and forth, it causes the air immediately next to it to be alternately compressed and rarified. One possible pattern of changes in air pressure over time, measured at a fixed distance from the sound source, is shown in Figure 1B. This pattern is the simplest form of re-

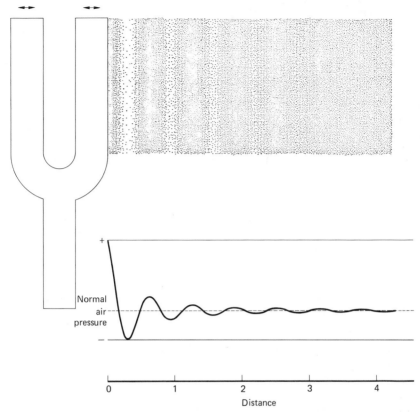

Figure 1A. *A tuning fork, showing the propagation of regions of higher-than-normal and lower-than-normal air pressure away from one of the vibrating arms. Propagated changes in air pressure diminish in amplitude as a function of distance from a sound source. The amplitude reduction is described by the* inverse-square law *(pressure is inversely proportioned to the square of the distance from the sound source).*

peating movement, in the sense that it is the type of vibration which results when a single mass is set into motion; and the resistance to its movement increases with the distance moved. The amplitude is smaller for the dashed line than for the solid one, meaning that the sound represented by the dashed line is the less intense of the two. Both waveforms consist of repeating patterns that begin at zero (or zero difference from normal air pressure), then rise to a maximum, diminish through zero to a minimum, and then return to zero. This sequence is one cycle of this particular waveform. In any waveform consisting of a single pattern repeated over and over, one repetition is called a *cycle*. The number of cycles per second is called the *frequency* of the sound. "Cycles per second," in modern writings, are called *Hertz* after the discoverer of the length and velocity of electro-

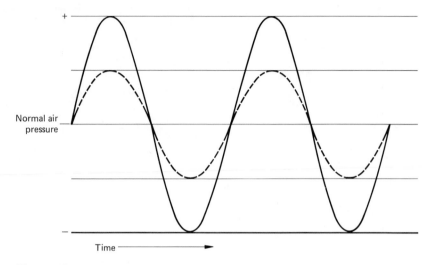

Figure 1B. *Changes in air pressure over time, as measured at a fixed distance from a sound source. The frequency of the sound is the number of single cycles occurring in one second. The dotted and solid waveforms thus have the same frequency, but differ by a factor of two in peak pressure.*

magnetic waves, Heinrich Hertz (1857-1894), and are usually abbreviated "Hz." But a single sound can have more than one frequency in it as shown in Figure 2A. The peculiar looking waveform shown at the top represents the pattern of change in air pressure that would arrive at your ear if two tuning forks were struck simultaneously, one with a resonant frequency of 1000 Hz and another with a resonant frequency of 2000 Hz. The individual waveforms produced by the two tuning forks are shown below. The complex waveform is actually the algebraic sum of the two simple waveforms, added point by point over time. Study this figure carefully. If you understand it thoroughly, the rest of this brief discussion on the physics of sound will be much easier. You might try adding a pair of waveforms yourself. Draw one under the other, using a piece of graph paper, then add the ordinate values (heights) of the two together, one point at a time. You will quickly discover that there are three ways one of the component waveforms can be varied to change the form of the final composite waveform. You can change either the frequency, the amplitude, or the point in its cycle at which one of the component waveforms begins. This last is called the starting *phase* of the waveform. Frequency, amplitude, and phase are the three primary characteristics of any repetitive waveform. The repetitive waveforms we have mainly been concerned with so far have been *sine waves,* like those shown in Figure 1. The sine wave is important in the study of hearing for two reasons: (1) It describes the simplest type of vibratory motion.

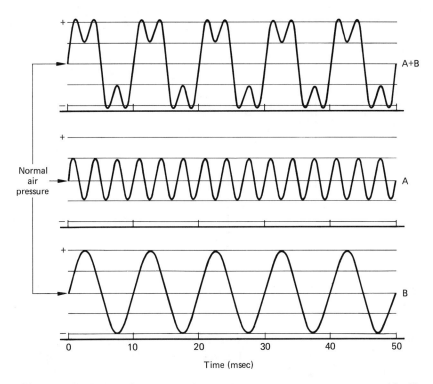

Figure 2A. *A complex waveform (A+B) and its two components (A, B). The sine wave components are shown with the relative intensities required to produce the complex waveform.*

(2) Any repetitive waveform, no matter how complex its shape, can be synthesized from a set of sine waves with specified frequencies and amplitudes. Any complex waveform may also be decomposed or analyzed into the set of sine waves of which it might be the sum. The mathematical technique for analyzing a waveform into its possible sinusoidal (sine-wave) components is called *Fourier analysis* after J. B. J. Fourier who derived it in 1822. The two sine waves in Figure 2A represent the results of a Fourier analysis if we applied it to the composite waveform. In analogy to the physics of light, Figure 2B is called an *acoustic spectrum.* It is another common way of describing the relative amplitude of each frequency present in the sound.

Because complex sounds can be synthesized into sinusoidal components does not mean that they were necessarily generated by adding sine waves together or that the ear functions as a Fourier analyzer. But it is an extremely convenient way to talk about complicated sounds, like those of human speech, a jet plane, or an oboe; and there is great historical precedent for viewing sounds in this fashion. Any complex sound could also be analyzed into a set of

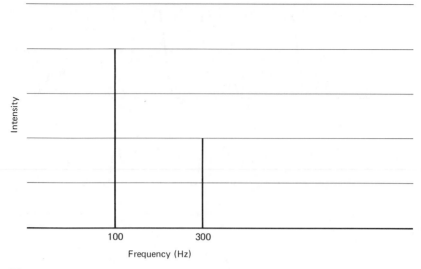

Figure 2B. *An acoustic spectrum, showing the frequencies and relative intensities of each component of the complex waveform.*

repetitive waves of virtually any form of which it could be the sum.

G. S. Ohm, for whom the basic law of electrical relationships is named, also proposed a law of hearing, based on the idea of the sinusoidal composition of all sounds. Ohm's acoustic law stated that animal and human ears function by somehow decomposing complex sounds into their sine-wave components. Helmholtz later suggested that this might be accomplished through a simple *resonance* principle. When set into motion, as by being struck with a hammer, most bodies tend to vibrate or resonate at a fixed fundamental frequency. The resonant frequency depends on the mass of the body to be set into motion and the restoring force which opposes that motion. These relationships are too complex to be discussed here, but they are generally treated in an introductory freshman physics course. For our purposes it is sufficient to understand that if the body to be set into motion consists of a mass whose movement is opposed by a restoring force (as a weight hanging on a coiled spring), it tends to vibrate in a sinusoidal fashion when force is applied to move it from its resting position. If the situation is more complex, as for example the many semi-independent masses represented by the body of a violin, then it will vibrate in a complex pattern, which may be analyzed into sinusoidal components of many different frequencies. As we shall see later, Helmholtz assumed that the inner ear performs a spectral analysis on complex sounds by acting as a set of resonating masses, each of which was "excited" by one of the component frequencies in a sound. Later research has disproved Helmholtz's resonance theory of hearing, but discovering its weaknesses was the major path to understanding how the ear actually functions.

UNITS OF MEASUREMENT OF SOUNDS

We have said that the major characteristics of a repetitive waveform are its frequency, intensity, and phase. It is important that we have convenient units for expressing the magnitude of each of these.

Frequency, as we have already suggested, is generally measured as the number of repetitions of the basic waveform in one second, cycles per second or Hz. By the "frequency range audible to human listeners," we generally mean those frequencies that a healthy young human ear can hear, about 20 to 20,000 Hz.

The intensity of sound is generally expressed in terms of the ratio of the sound pressure to be measured to a standard reference pressure. The generally accepted reference is 0.0002 dynes per square centimeter (many other references are occasionally used, all interrelated by appropriate physical relations). This reference is close to the weakest pressure audible to a normal listener. The basic unit of measurement is the *bel,* named in honor of Alexander Graham Bell (1847–1922), the American scientist and inventor of the telephone. The sound pressures that cause pain or even deafness are about ten million times greater than the weakest pressure we can hear. This would mean an awkward measurement system for the science that must deal with this entire "dynamic range," and the solution has been to define the bel in logarithmic terms. A sound whose level is one bel is ten times the level of the reference, one of two bels is one hundred times the level of the reference. Since this scale is coarse, it was given a finer grain by introducing the *decibel* (dB), one tenth of a bel. The ten million-to-one range of sound pressures mentioned above corresponds to approximately 140 dB. When the word *level* is used in describing the intensive dimension of a sound, it is generally assumed that the unit of measurement is the decibel. The most common intensive scale—the one for which 0.0002 dynes/cm^2 is the reference—is the sound-pressure-level scale, usually abbreviated SPL.

This discussion has avoided a minor complication in the relation between a reference pressure and the decibel. It is this. Sound pressure over a square area (pressure squared) is proportional to *sound power,* and the bel is defined as a *power ratio.* This means that the level of a sound in bels is given by the formula

$$\text{level } (\textit{in bels}) = \log_{10}\left(\frac{\text{sound power to be measured}}{\text{a reference power}}\right)$$

$$\text{and level } (\textit{in decibels}) = 10\log_{10}\left(\frac{\text{sound power to be measured}}{\text{a reference power}}\right).$$

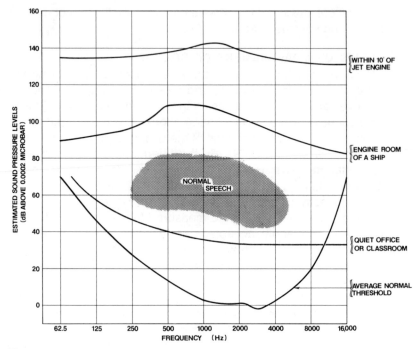

Figure 3. *The auditory area (area above threshold of hearing for humans) and some representative levels of familiar sounds shown in relation to this area.*

But since power is proportional to the square of pressure, sound level in decibels can either be calculated as ten times the logarithm of a power ratio or 20 times the corresponding pressure ratio. The only sleight of hand required is that you remember that

$$\log A^K = K \log A,$$

and therefore if

$$10 \log (\text{power ratio}) = 10 \log (\text{pressure ratio})^2$$

then

$$10 \log (\text{power ratio}) = 20 \log (\text{pressure ratio}).$$

A pressure ratio of 10:1 is therefore a 20 dB ratio; a pressure ratio of 100:1 is a 40 dB ratio; and a pressure ratio of 2:1 is about 6 dB. Most important, remember that these measurements in decibels are always ratios of two sound levels; and unless the reference is specified, a level in decibels tells nothing whatsoever about the absolute intensity of a sound. Sound levels can be understood easily in terms of familiar examples; a few are shown in Figure 3.

The phase of a sound is measured in terms of the elementary

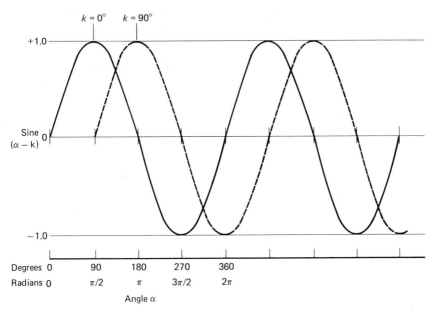

Figure 4A. *Two sine waves with a 90° or π/2 radian difference in starting phase. The solid line is the sine of the angles shown along the abscissa; the dotted line is the sine of the angles less 90°.*

repetitive component of that sound. In the case of the sine wave, this component is one sinusoidal cycle as shown in Figure 4A.

The dotted waveform in the figure begins when the solid waveform is already one-quarter of the way through its cycle. This is called a *phase shift* or *phase difference* of either 90° or π/2 radians. Recall that a circle is divided into 360° or 2π radians. The use of this terminology stems from the definition of the sine wave as the ratio of the height of a point on the circumference of a circle (with center at y = x = o) to the radius of the circle. As the point moves around the circle the sine wave is generated, as illustrated in Figure 4B.

NOISE

One other class of sounds has been important to the study of human hearing. It is a special type of noise. *Noise* is sometimes defined as any unwanted or uncontrolled fluctuation in anything. Random fluctuations in air pressure are thus "auditory noise." Noise can be intentionally produced in which a wide range of frequencies is present, each with an amplitude that varies randomly from instant to instant. Such noise has the sound of steam escaping or of a television receiver tuned to a channel that has gone off the air. Noises containing only selected frequency ranges can be produced by passing *broadband noise* through special narrow-band filters. The power

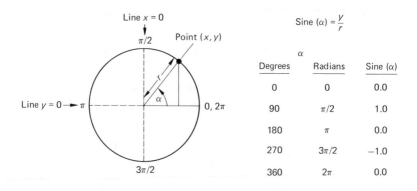

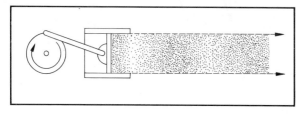

Figure 4B. *Illustration of the relation between circular motion and a sine wave. As the dot revolves around the circle, the sine of the angle, α, produces the sine wave as shown in the table. One manner in which such circular motion may yield sinusoidal changes in air pressure is shown by the drive wheel and piston mechanism in the inset.*

spectrum of a noise is a line, the height of which represents the average amplitude of the noise at each frequency.

AUDITORY PHYSIOLOGY AND ANATOMY

Sensory receptors are specialized parts of the nervous system that are particularly sensitive to one form of energy known as the adequate stimulus for that sensory modality. The adequate stimulus for the auditory system is, of course, acoustic pressure in the ear canal. From our personal experience it is clear that the auditory system must accomplish at least two major functions. First, it must translate small changes in air pressure into neural responses. Second, it must have a way of responding differently to those several dimensions of sounds that we can obviously distinguish. The system that does these things consists of the "peripheral receptor mechanisms," the "auditory cortex," and a complex system of interconnections between the two. A great deal of research effort has been concentrated on the peripheral receptor mechanisms during the past 50 years. This work has provided a detailed, although still incomplete, picture

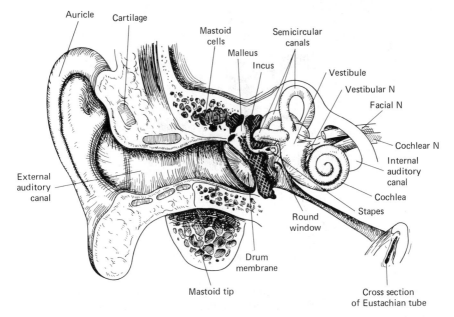

Figure 5. *The inner, middle, and outer human ear. The temporal bone has been cut away to reveal the semicircular canals and the cochlea. The musculature of the middle ear is omitted. [From* Hearing and Deafness, *3d ed., by Hallowell Davis and Richard Silverman. Copyright © 1947, 1960, 1970 by Holt, Rinehart, and Winston, Inc. Reprinted by permission of Holt, Rinehart and Winston.]*

of the way sounds are translated into neural activity. Work on the higher stages of the system is still in its infancy.

THE PERIPHERAL RECEPTOR MECHANISMS

The peripheral receptor for hearing consists of the three parts of the ear, conventionally called the outer, middle, and inner ear as shown in Figure 5. Man's outer ear, known as the *pinna,* has lost many of the functions that it probably once had. In animals, it still serves to collect sound and actively direct it into the ear canal, as you can see by walking through a zoo, snapping your fingers or whistling at various animals. Many species will turn their pinnae toward the source of the sound, rather than their whole heads. Some species, particularly those that spend parts of their lives underground or in water, can also use parts of the external ear to close off the ear canal, to protect it from extreme pressures or from foreign matter. The pinna's function for man was formerly considered to be primarily esthetic, but recent evidence has shown that it plays a significant role in locating sound sources on the median plane.

The middle ear's role is important, however, for without its operation hearing is severely degraded. The middle ear consists of the

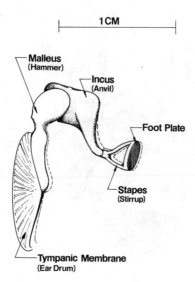

1 CM

Malleus
(Hammer)

Incus
(Anvil)

Foot Plate

Stapes
(Stirrup)

Tympanic Membrane
(Ear Drum)

Figure 6. *Ossicles of the middle ear, shown with their normal modes of movement in response to pressure changes in the ear canal.*

cavity between the eardrum or *tympanic membrane* and the outer wall of the snail-shaped cochlea. The contents of this cavity are shown diagrammatically in Figure 6 and consist of three small bones or *ossicles.* These are known as the *hammer, anvil,* and *stirrup* (or *malleus, incus,* and *stapes)* because of their general shapes. The ossicles act to translate large, but not very forceful movements of the eardrum into smaller, but higher pressure movements of the stapes at the end of the ossicular chain. This translation is accomplished by a slight lever action by which swinging the long arm of the malleus causes the stapes to press in and out, like a piston. This action leads to a transmission of airborne sound into a corresponding pattern of changing pressures on the fluids that lie on the inner-ear side of the stapes.

The ossicles have certain protective features built into them that seem to help avoid the potentially damaging effects of intense sound. Perhaps the most important of these is that the movement of the stapes is limited by the *annular ligament,* which surrounds its base or footplate. This ligament will not allow the piston-like move-ment to exceed certain limits. The entire ossicular chain can also be-come much stiffer if two small muscles (the stapedius muscle and the tensor tympani) which are attached to the stapes are caused to con-tract. This stiffening leads to less efficient conduction of energy into the delicate regions of the inner ear. One of the most interesting features of the middle ear is that these two small muscles are under the control of the central nervous system. If we make a loud sound in

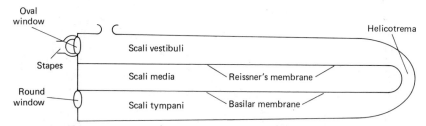

Figure 7. *Highly diagramatic view of the cochlear duct as it might appear if its spiral were "uncoiled" to form an elongated tube. While helpful in understanding the transmission of hydraulic pressure changes from the stapes into the fluid-filled ducts, this type of diagram cannot accurately portray the actual positions or sizes of the major cochlear structures.*

one of a person's ears, the protective muscular response can be measured in the other.

The inner ear is a set of fluid-filled cavities in the temporal bone as shown in Figure 5. The *cochlea* is the main receptor organ for hearing. The other cavities, the *semicircular canals,* are the receptors for sensing the direction of movement and gravitational pull. We will not say much on the function of the semicircular canals, except that dizziness and certain types of auditory pathology tend to occur together (e.g. some forms of hearing disorders have dizziness as a concurrent symptom).

The easiest way to understand the cochlea is to uncoil the snail-shaped cavity and examine it in side view, as a tube about one inch long, and then look at the cross section of that tube as shown in Figures 7 and 8. The cochlea has two lengthwise partitions that separate the tube into three divisions, or *scalae* (Figure 7). These partitions are seen most clearly in the cross-sectional diagram in Figure 8, from Davis and Silverman, and are called the *basilar membrane* and *Reissner's membrane.* These two membranes come together about a millimeter short of the end of the cochlear "tube" and form a closed compartment separating the *endolymphatic fluid* between them from the *perilymphatic fluid* in the remainder of the cochlea. The space between the two membranes is called the *scala media,* that above them is the *scala vestibuli,* and that below, the *scala tympani.* The small passage connecting the scala tympani to the scala vestibuli at the end of the tube is called the *helicotrema.*

The actual neural receptors for hearing consist of a network of cells supported by the basilar membrane and which together are known as the organ of Corti. Some of the details of this organ are shown in Figure 8, from Davis and Silverman. The primary receptor cells are the *hair cells,* which are arranged in rows—three rows on one side of a supporting structure called the *rods of Corti,* and one

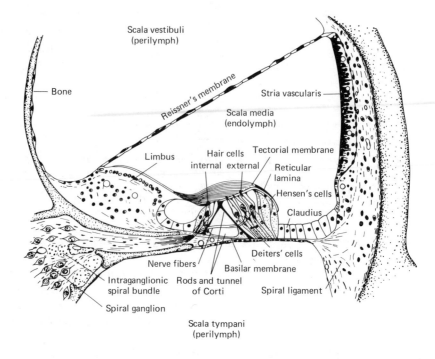

Figure 8. *Cross section of the cochlea. [From Davis and Silverman, 1970.]*

row on the other side. Surrounding the hair cells are other cells that apparently serve to support and protect them. The hair cells project a short distance into the *tectorial membrane,* which can slide back and forth slightly, thus placing mechanical stress on the hair cells. The entire organ of Corti is supported rigidly by the bony shelf to which it is attached on one side (the side toward the central axis of the "snail") and more flexibly by the spiral ligaments to which it is attached on the other side (the side toward the outer shell of the snail). The hair cells have many synaptic connections, both with other hair cells and with the (afferent) auditory nerve cells, whose nuclei are nearby in the spiral ganglion. The hair cells also have many connections with efferent fibers, whose function is to conduct impulses to the cochlea from the more central portions of the nervous system. The exact role played by these efferent fibers is still unclear.

The organ of Corti is about an inch long, as we said earlier, but its width varies considerably from one end to the other. At the end closest to the stapes, called the *basal turn,* it is only 0.04 mm in width. At the far end, it is almost 0.5 mm wide.

Given this picture of cochlear anatomy, how is pressure on the foot plate of the stapes turned into neural activity? The earliest theory that made use of a fairly detailed understanding of cochlear anatomy was the resonance theory proposed by Helmholtz. He assumed that the cochlea must accomplish the analysis of complex sounds into sinusoidal components, as proposed by Ohm's Acoustic Law. One way that this could be done might be for the basilar membrane to be divided into regions with various resonant frequencies, much like the strings in a piano. The wider portion of the membrane would probably act as would longer strings and thus resonate in response to lower frequencies, while the narrower part would respond to the higher frequencies. Not until the Nobel-prize winning research of Georg von Békésy was it clear that Helmholtz was on the right track, but was wrong in many of the critical details.

The basilar membrane does not move in sympathetic vibration when pressure changes are introduced into the scalae from the action of the stapes. The membrane is not tightly enough stretched, nor has it the correct dimensions or mass to resonate at the frequencies to which it is primarily sensitive, as Helmholtz had proposed. Instead, the pressure changes which are introduced into the perilymph spread quickly to the end of the tube, exerting force against the membrane. But the narrow portion of the membrane toward its basal end is displaced more rapidly than the wider portions closer to the apical end. The effect is that a wavelength motion (progressive vertical displacement) travels down the length of the membrane as shown in Figure 9. The traveling wave reaches a maximum amplitude at some point along the membrane. When stimulated by a brief pulse or by a high frequency waveform, this point of maximum deformation of the membrane is toward the basal end. When stimulated by a long pulse or by a low-frequency waveform the maximum deformation occurs toward the apical end. Assuming that maximum deformation means maximum stimulation of the hair cells, this then provides the mechanism that Helmholtz was looking for. Acoustic frequencies can thus be decoded into different *places* of activity along the basilar membrane. We will return to *place theory* and its alternatives in a later section.

The proposition that maximum deformation of the membrane leads to maximum hair-cell response seems reasonable, although the mechanism by which the neural responses are generated is still not clear. When a sound is introduced into the ear, one of its effects is to cause an electrical potential difference between the endolymph and the perilymph, called the *cochlear microphonic* (CM). This electrical response is a high fidelity copy of the stimulating acoustic waveform. Because the CM is strongest in the region of the cochlea where the traveling wave has maximum amplitude, it is suspected that it may be produced by the hair cells themselves. This electrical replica of the acoustic waveform may then in turn help to trigger the all-or-none responses of the second order neural cells. The actual

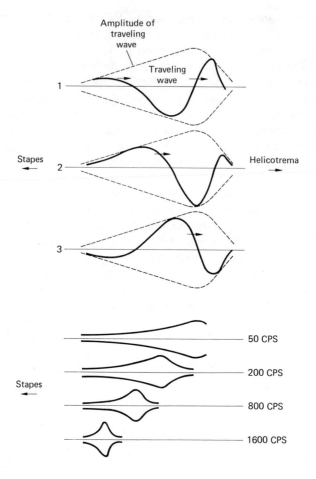

Figure 9. *"Traveling wave" motion of the basilar membrane as described by von Békésy. The lower section shows that the envelopes of the traveling wave for various sound frequencies have maxima that are closer to the stapes for higher frequencies.* [*From* Man's World of Sound, *copyright © 1958 by John R. Pierce and Edward E. David, Jr. Reprinted by permission of Doubleday & Co., Inc.*]

sequence of events is still under investigation, but one fact is clear. The CM probably plays a major role in the reception of sound because anything which suppresses it also suppresses the action of the higher portions of the auditory system.

SINGLE-CELL AUDIOGRAMS

An audiogram is a graph showing the sensitivity of a system or subsystem to various frequencies of sound, that is, the minimum

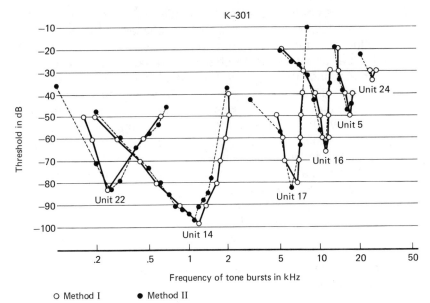

O Method I   ● Method II

Figure 10. *Single-nerve audiograms for individual fibers in the cat's audi-tory nerve. The solid and dashed lines represent small variations in the experimental procedure.* [*From* Discharge Patterns of Single Fibers in the Cat's Auditory Nerve, *by N. Y.-S. Kiang, Research Monograph No. 35, 1965, M.I.T. Press. Reprinted by permission of The M.I.T. Press, Cambridge, Mass.*]

sound level required to elicit a response at each frequency. The most common such graph is for the whole organism and shows the sensi-tivity indicated by a behavioral response to each test frequency. In simpler terms, this means the results of a hearing test. But auditory physiologists have also developed excellent techniques for measur-ing the sensitivity of single nerve cells in many parts of the auditory system. Typical single-nerve audiograms for single fibers in the audi-tory nerve are shown in Figure 10, by N. Y.-S. Kiang. There is a sin-gle frequency to which each cell is maximally sensitive, that is, to which it responds at a minimum sound level. As the level of the sound is raised, the cells respond to a wider range of frequencies.

The threshold, or level of sound to which a single cell will re-spond, usually means the minimum sound level to which it will re-spond above its average spontaneous rate. (Most cells in the nervous system respond now and then without apparent reason, an important fact to remember.) To the physiologists' dismay, the animals' behav-ioral thresholds are 20 to 30 dB *lower* (more sensitive) than the thresholds of auditory nerve cells measured in this way. However, there is another way of looking at the data obtained from a single-cell recording. It was noticed that the cell tended to respond with an all-or-none electrical impulse only at certain phases of the stimulating wave. In fact they tend to respond no more than once in each cycle, and always at about the same phase. The recordings of single-cell activity in response to sounds weaker than those which increase the response rate have been reexamined with these facts in mind. By using a computer to help analyze the data, it was discovered that even at very weak sound levels there were changes in the average interpulse intervals. A typical graph of this result is shown in Figure 11; it is called an interpulse interval histogram. What this figure demonstrates is that not only does a sound lead to more neural responding, but it also causes the normal number of spontaneous responses to take on a systematic temporal pattern. This pattern is clearly a tendency to respond at intervals of about one cycle of the frequency of the stimulating sound. Sound levels at which the neural responses take on a recognizable temporal pattern are closer to the behavioral thresholds than are the sound levels that increase the neural firing rates.

PHYSIOLOGICAL RESPONSES
TO THE BASIC DIMENSIONS OF SOUND

As we said at the beginning of this discussion, the structure of the nervous system must somehow account for both the absolute sensitivity of hearing and also its *resolving power* or the ability to distinguish between sounds to which we are clearly sensitive.

Resolution of sound level. Physiologists have not yet discovered the form of neural encoding for the intensive dimension of auditory stimuli. We can conjecture that one reason for this failure might be that the evolutionary pressures on the auditory system lead it to be specialized for other characteristics of sounds, particularly their spectra and longer-term temporal properties, and perhaps to pay less attention to sound level. (Sound levels vary so much with the distance from source to receiver that how loud a sound is seldom tells a listener very much about what made it.) The psychophysical facts of auditory resolving power are at least moderately consistent with this conjecture. We can notice, as we have remarked elsewhere, a quarter of a percent change in the frequency of a tone, we can detect a reversal of the order of a sound when that sound is as brief as 2 msec in duration, but the intensity of the sound must be changed by 10 percent or more for us to notice that change. However, we do in fact experience a continuous growth of the sensation of loudness as sound pressures are increased over a range of about 120 dB. How does the auditory system encode this broad dynamic range?

Two obvious schemes by which sound intensity might be en-

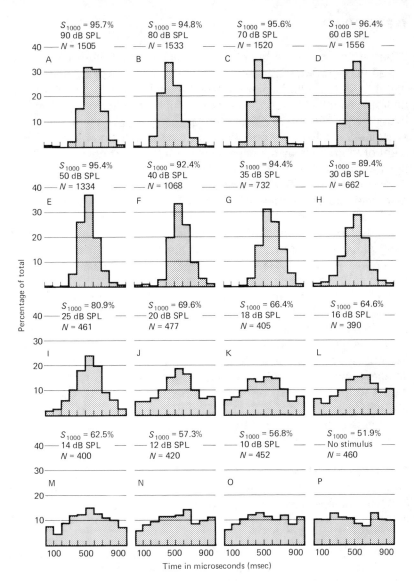

Figure 11. *Pulse-interval histograms showing the "time-locking" (tendency to respond at a particular time after stimulus onset) of neural responses in a single auditory nerve fiber of the squirrel monkey. As the sound pressure is increased from no input whatsoever to 25 dB SPL, there is no significant increase in the total number of neural spike responses (N). However, the percent of the responses (S) that could be included in a half-cycle of the stimulus frequency (from 250 to 750 msec) increases from the "chance" rate of 50 to 80 percent as the stimulus is raised in level over this same range. If the animals are behaviorally sensitive to sounds below 25 dB SPL, this would suggest that, in this range, the stimulus is encoded by neural time-locking rather than by overall neural discharge rate. [From J. E. Rose et al., Phase-locked response to low-frequency tones in single auditory nerve fibers of the squirrel monkey, J. Neurophysiol., 1967, 30, 769–793.] Reprinted by permission.*

coded in the output of cochlear cells are (1) that more cells could fire as the sound was made more intense, or (2) that the same cells might fire more often. Unfortunately, the facts gathered in single-unit neurophysiological recordings do not support either of these simple hypotheses. The range of thresholds of individual cells is not broad enough for the intensity encoding to be accomplished by the recruitment of more cells as stimulus level is raised. That cells typically do not fire with more than one neural discharge per stimulus period means that the encoding cannot be accomplished by raising the response rate of a single cell. Current physiological studies point toward some more complex form of coding, by which the level of the stimulus may be represented either in the spatial pattern of cells firing along the length of the basilar membrane or in the temporal pattern of responses (e.g., possibly in the increasing synchrony among responses of nearby cells as the stimulus level is raised). One aspect of cochlear activity that does change systematically with sound level is the amplitude of the cochlear microphonic, but as we suggested earlier, the physiological role played by this graded response is still not completely understood. Further up in the auditory nervous system it is clear that increasing sound level does register its effect, since the level of the elicited electrical activity that can be recorded from the cortical region of the human brain, using surface electrodes, is highly correlated with the level of an eliciting sound. But the search for the primary neural correlate of sound level in the peripheral nervous system continues.

Resolution of sound frequency. One of the old problems in the science of hearing was the apparent inconsistency between the small differences in frequency that are obvious to a listener and the broad excitation patterns on the basilar membrane caused by a pure tone. If, as Helmholtz assumed, the ear encodes sound frequency by stimulating different places along the basilar membrane, why does it not confuse two tones whose excitation patterns overlap each other by 90 to 95 percent? One possible answer to this question is that the cells actually encode the stimulus frequency in temporal patterns of interpulse intervals, as well as by the place of the neural activity. The data in Figure 11 showed that receptor cells do transmit information about the duration of a single cycle on to higher portions of the auditory system. But it is also possible that the nervous system can perform an accurate calculation of the average place of response and thus make precise judgments of stimulus frequency using only place information. The most recent evidence points to frequency coding in terms of interpulse intervals, but this story is not yet complete.

The encoding of frequency is at least partially a matter of the place of maximum stimulation; of this we are certain for many reasons. The cochlear microphonic is strongest near the part of the basilar membrane where the stimulus frequency leads to maximum activity. Intense sounds tend to destroy parts of the organ of Corti that correspond to their frequency. Animals discovered to have regions of hair cells missing (at autopsy) had reduced sensitivity for sounds whose frequencies lead to maximum activity in those regions.

Some other factors suggest that there must be considerably more to frequency analysis than can be completely handled by place theories. Evidence favoring the alternative, *periodicity theories* of frequency processing, is mainly behavioral rather than physiological, however; so that discussion appears later.

HIGHER PORTIONS OF THE AUDITORY SYSTEM

Most of the pathways from the cochlea to the other parts of the central nervous system (CNS) have been known for many years, but we are not at all sure what the functions of all of the various paths and way stations are. Figure 12 shows many of these pathways. The olivary nucleus is a particularly interesting neural site in that it is the most peripheral point in the auditory system which receives inputs from both ears. As such it has been proposed as a point at which the arrival time of sounds at the two ears may be compared.

From the olivary nucleus, the main auditory pathway goes up to the lateral lemniscus, to the medial geniculate body, and finally to the auditory cortex. Studies of the effects of tumors and accidental brain damage, plus data from research with animals, support the following general picture of the functioning of this system. Complex processing seems to occur at higher levels. Simple detection of sounds or discrimination of two very unlike sounds can be accomplished without an intact auditory cortex. But fine discrimination or identification of sounds requires that the entire system be working properly as a unit. When damage to one part of a system causes it to malfunction in a particular way, we are sometimes tempted to conclude that the damaged region was the "center" for the now-absent function. Similar oversimplified reasoning could lead to the conclusion that the distributor cap is the center for controlling the operation of a car's engine. As techniques are developed for single-cell recording and stimulation in intact animals, we may learn that many auditory functions are not accomplished by specific centers, but by the integrated operation of the entire system.

The cortex of man has no clear left-right dominance with respect to hearing in general, probably because inputs from both ears terminate at left and right auditory cortex. It has been known for about one hundred years, however, that the left hemisphere has some

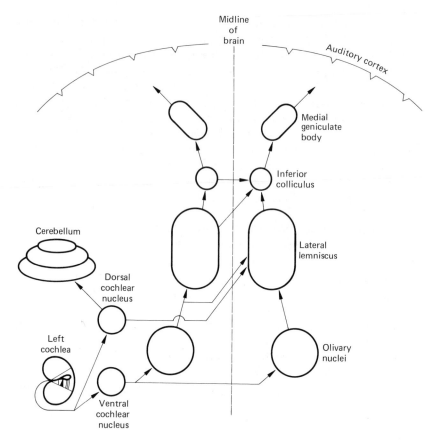

Figure 12. *Ascending pathways in the auditory nervous system. The arrows show the pathways along which information can move from the organ of Corti in the left cochlea to the auditory cortex. It is important to note that the corresponding pathways from the right cochlea are not drawn here.* [*Adapted from Whitfield, I. C. Centrifugal control mechanism of the auditory pathway. In A. V. S. de Renck and Julie Knight (Eds.),* Hearing mechanism in vertebrates. *Ciba Foundation Symposium. London: J & A. Churchill, 1968.*)]

special involvement in both the perception and production of speech. Severe damage to the parietal area (roughly one inch or so above the ear) of the left hemisphere can cause loss of speech perception, production, or both. Electrical stimulation of this general area, on the right hemisphere, during operations, has led the patients to report hearing complex nonspeech sounds or even melodies. It is too early to weave these kinds of results into a complete theory of hearing, but they point to very complex processing and integration at the higher levels of the central nervous system (CNS).

FUNDAMENTAL PSYCHOACOUSTIC MEASUREMENTS

To this point, we have been talking about sound and about the neuroanatomical basis of hearing; now we are ready for hearing itself. Hearing, to a nonscientist, is reasonably thought of as the mechanism by which physical sounds become sounds in consciousness. Unfortunately, this manner of thinking leads to questions like, "If a tree falls in the forest, does it make any sound if no one is there to hear it?" From the subjective point of view, there are two answers to this question. One is that if sound only exists in human conscious awareness, then no, there obviously is no sound. The other is another version of the consciousness-is-primary approach: if we can only be certain that sounds exist by perceiving them, then the conditions of the example make the answer unobtainable.

In the midnineteenth century, experimental psychologists realized that thousands of years of this style of conjecture had produced many provocative questions, but few answers. At about that time some philosophers interested in the human senses began to stress the idea that a meaningful scientific question is one that is potentially answerable. By this, they meant that the procedures by which evidence was gathered should be capable of being repeated by any interested scientist and that the evidence should be open to inspection through means other than private introspection. As an early psychologist and auditory theorist, Max Meyer, saw the issue, we had made about all the progress possible through studying our personal perceptions. He felt another approach was needed: we should concentrate on *the psychology of the other one.* Meyer meant, of course, that we would collect much less ambiguous evidence if we concentrated on measuring other peoples' responses to sounds than if we only looked inwardly at the goings-on in our own heads. Here we try to abide by Meyer's suggestion, although the reader will see that this doesn't mean that we must avoid psychological concepts like *loudness* and *pitch.* What it does mean is that although the subjective nature of loudness is unavailable for direct examination, we have learned a great deal about the way normally hearing people use the word. For example, "twice as loud" means an increase in sound pressure of about 10 dB to most people (recall that 6 dB would be a physical doubling of pressure).

We concentrate on two objective aspects of human hearing. The first is called *sensory capability;* that is, sensitivity, resolving power, channel capacity, and memory. These are the fundamental properties of any sensory system and are measured (or more properly *estimated* since they are theoretical limits), by normal listeners' performance in detecting, discriminating, and identifying sounds. None of these operations appears to be specifically related to memory, but memory is involved in each of them. Sensory capabilities thus spell out what we *can* do with our sensory apparatus.

The other aspect of hearing can be called *response proclivities,* the characteristic ways people respond to sounds, even though a variety of other responses are clearly within their capability. Most of what might be considered the psychological part of the science of hearing deals with *proclivities* rather than *capabilities,* but the two are not always easily distinguished. The proclivity-capability distinction is discussed at length in a chapter in the Handbook of General Psychology (Watson, 1973).

AUDITORY SENSORY CAPABILITIES

Sensitivity. The first sensory capability is *simple sensitivity* or the ability to detect the presence of a sound. Many experiments have been conducted to determine just how sensitive the human listener can be, that is, to measure the minimum audible pressure (MAP). Figure 13 shows the results of an experiment conducted by the author and his co-workers, along with two international standard estimates of the MAP. All three sets of data show the same general facts. Man is able to hear weak sounds between the frequencies of 1000 and 2000 Hz. But as the frequency is reduced from 1000 to 125 Hz, the sound pressure must be increased by about 30 dB if it is to remain audible. This figure shows data only to 4000 Hz, because most of the sounds of importance to human listeners are below this frequency. This is fortunate, for at higher frequencies the sound pressure must again be raised if the sound is to remain audible. In a typical healthy young adult a sound pressure level of more than 80 dB is required to hear sounds above 10,000 Hz. The upper-frequency limit of sensitivity is often said to be 20,000 Hz. What this actually means is that we cannot generate sounds intense enough to be heard above this frequency with normal testing equipment. Nor would we want to, because of the potential damage that such sound levels may cause to the human ear.

In Figure 13, from Watson, et al (1972), it can be seen that different experiments have apparently produced differing estimates of normal sensitivity. The reason for this is partly that some testing methods yield higher estimates of sensitivity than others. Also, older investigations used fairly naive listeners, who were asked to hold up your finger when you hear the tone. Newer methods use highly trained listeners, who are typically tested in some form of *forced-choice psychophysical method.* In the forced-choice methods the listener may be told, for example, that a light will flash twice on each trial and

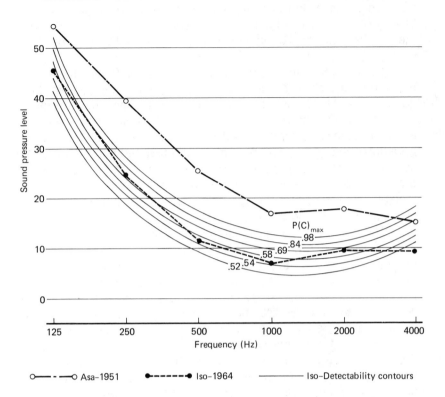

Figure 13. *Three estimates of the minimum audible pressure for normal human listeners. The American Standards Association (ASA) and the International Standards Organization (ISO) curves represent "best estimates" based on the work of several different laboratories. The solid lines show the average sound pressures associated with various levels of performance in a forced-choice listening task for 12 highly trained listeners. [After Watson et al. Detection of tones in the absence of external masking noise. J. of the Acoust. Soc. of Am. 1972, 52, 633–643. Reprinted by permission.]*

that a faint tone will always be present during one of the two flashes. After each trial he must decide during which of the two flashes the sound was present. The smooth curves in Figure 13 represent the sound levels at which highly trained listeners could achieve various percentages of correct judgments under this procedure. Data from the modern methods have generally shown the sensory capabilities of listeners to be more acute than the older methods; and on this basis alone, they must be judged more valid estimates of what we can do with our ears. But there is no similarly simple criterion by which we can evaluate methods for measuring response proclivities. The capability-proclivity distinction and the proper operations by which these two aspects of sense-based behavior are measured are best understood in terms of the contemporary body of knowledge called the Theory of Signal Detectability. That theory is most completely summarized in texts by Green and Swets (1966, 1974), and by Egan (1975).

The minimum audible pressures described in Figure 13 were all measured for tone pulses that were one-quarter of a second in duration or longer. Briefer pulses cannot be heard unless they are raised above the levels shown here. This reflects the ability of the ear, like all other sensory systems, to add energy over time. Auditory "temporal integration" goes on over about the first 150 milliseconds of a sound. A 16-millisecond pulse must be about 12 to 14 dB higher in pressure than a 250-millisecond pulse for the two to be equally detectable. However, being equally detectable does not mean that the two sounds will be indiscriminable.

Thus far we have talked about the lower limit of sound pressures to which normal listeners are sensitive. To make a simple picture many scientists have also proposed an upper limit, although the existence of such is based more in rational analysis than experimental measurements. As sound levels are raised, somewhere between 120 and 140 dB SPL, most listeners will retire from the experiment, and they should. Sound levels appreciably lower than those called too loud to be tolerated by most people can be dangerous to the delicate structures of the inner ear. The maximum levels of sounds to which man can be exposed without danger are currently under intense investigation. Conservative estimates place these damage-risk criteria at 100 dB SPL for periodic sounds and 80 dB SPL for continuous ones.

The potential for auditory damage represented by a sound depends on several factors in addition to its pressure level. These include its spectrum, duration, and the way the total duration is distributed in time. Research on these matters is difficult. It must depend on laboratory studies in which animals are exposed to various sounds and on the retrospective analysis of the sounds to which people with hearing loss have been exposed. Both types of study have built-in flaws. No animal ear is precisely like that of the human being. Retrospective studies can only yield educated guesses about the sounds any single person has been exposed to over a period of years. Nevertheless, the cumulative results of many human and animal studies now provide a reasonable basis for estimating the range of sounds to which we can be safely exposed. J. D. Miller (1974) summarized these data.

RESOLVING POWER

The second major aspect of sensory capability is resolving power or the precision with which one sound can be discriminated from an-

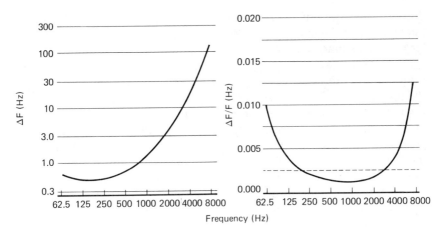

Figure 14. *Two ways of displaying the human listener's ability to distinguish between the frequencies of tones. The left panel illustrates the increase in the just-detectable increment (Δf) as the frequency (f) is raised. The right panel illustrates the degree to which these results are described by a constant Weber ratio (Δf/f). A Weber ratio of 0.0025 (dashed line) is a fairly good representation in the middle range of the ear's sensitivity, for example, 200–3000 Hz. [These figures are based on data reported by Harris (1952) and by Henning (1966).]*

other. Sounds can, of course, differ in many ways, but those that have been studied most thoroughly are differences of frequency, level, and duration. Figure 14 shows the differences in frequency that well-trained, normal listeners can discriminate at about 75 percent correct in a two-alternative forced-choice test. In the left-hand panel of this figure the just-detectable differences in frequency (Δf) are shown at each of the test frequencies (f). At the lower frequencies a 1 or 2 Hz change is just detectable, while at the higher frequencies the equally detectable differences can be as great as 10 to 15 Hz. Over the middle range of sensitivity, about 300 to 2500 Hz, the just-detectable values of Δf approximate a constant fraction of the frequency to which they are added or from which they are subtracted. This relationship is an example of one of the earliest laws in sensory psychology, which is named after a German scientist, E. H. Weber (1795–1878). Weber's Law states that a just-detectable change (ΔS) in a stimulus, S, tends to be a constant fraction of that stimulus, or ΔS/S = K. The Weber fraction or ratio of 0.0025 is represented by the horizontal dashed line in the right-hand panel of Figure 14. The original data plotted in the left-hand panel are thus fairly well described by the Weber constant in the mid-frequency region. At low and high frequencies, however, frequency-resolving power is not as acute, as reflected by the larger Weber ratios. The data shown here are for 75 dB SPL tones, which were 250 milliseconds (msec) in duration. When tones become very weak, within 10 to 15 dB of their minimum detectable levels, the Weber ratio increases, as it also does for tones less than 20 to 30 msec in duration.

We will not dwell on resolving power for level as much as for frequency, as the types of experiments are similar. Recall that the decibel measure is already a ratio. Therefore, if Weber's Law is valid for level discrimination, listeners should be able to discriminate a constant increment in level (ΔI) in decibels added to any starting level (I). This is an accurate prediction. The just-detectable increment in level is between 0.5 and 1.0 dB through most of the auditory range. For very weak sounds the just-detectable value of ΔI increases to 2.0 dB or more. (To calculate the Weber constant for intensity discrimination, remember that a 1.0 dB difference in pressure means that

$$20 \log \frac{P_1}{P_2} = 1.0. \text{ Therefore} \frac{P_1}{P_2} = 1.12, \text{ and} \frac{\Delta P}{P} \text{ is about } 0.12.)$$

The ability to discriminate the duration of sounds also can be summarized by the appropriate Weber ratio. For sounds whose durations range from about 20 to 200 msec, we can detect a change of duration of about 10 percent (a Weber ratio of 0.1).

One way of comparing resolving power for various dimensions of a sound is by the values of the Weber ratio for each dimension. Since these ratios are about 0.1 for duration and level and 0.0025 for frequency, it seems reasonable to claim that the ear is exquisitely capable as a frequency analyzer, but not nearly so accurate in resolving some other physical dimensions of sounds.

The capability to identify sounds is obviously related to the ability to discriminate between them. But here the system begins to run into the more general limitations of learning and memory, which are common to all sensory modalities. George Miller, in a famous paper, (1956) summarized many examples of observers' inability to cope with an identification task in which there were more than "seven, plus-or-minus-two" stimuli, which varied along only one physical dimension. Listeners can discriminate between frequencies of only a few Hz; therefore, an excess of 600 to 800 discriminable frequencies are in the auditory range. But a listener cannot be trained to identify more than seven or eight of these, no matter how far apart they are in frequency. However, listeners can learn to identify many more stimuli if they are allowed to vary along several physical dimensions, for example, in frequency, level, and duration.

The capability to remember complex sounds is generally good, as anyone who has listened to the "top ten" for many years can testify; perhaps you wish it were not so good at times. This ability may seem very acute, or not, depending on the method used to demonstrate it. The two basic methods are recognition and recall, just as in the study of memory for words or other stimuli. "Raw" memory is most clearly tested by methods that neither require the listener to reproduce the sound (by singing or twisting the dial on an oscillator) nor to recall a name for it. Both reproducing and naming might degrade his performance because of factors having nothing to do with his ability to store the effects of a sound. A procedure that measures memory without requiring reproduction or naming of the stimuli can be based on the forced-choice psychophysical methods discussed in the section on sensitivity. A set of 50 novel sounds is played for a listener today. Then tomorrow or next week, these 50 are intermixed with 50 other sounds; and the listener is asked to say whether he heard each sound in the first session. With such recognition-memory tests, it has been shown that observers' ability to remember both pictures and sounds is extremely accurate, much more so than the observers typically expect it to be. In one such experiment listeners scored better than 95 percent correct in picking out sounds they had only heard for a second or two, more than 24 hours earlier (Miller and Tanis, 1971).

Simultaneous masking. The capabilities described in the preceding section show human hearing to be a potentially efficient way to acquire information. We can detect changes in air pressure that cause the eardrum to be displaced about as far as the diameter of a hydrogen atom. We can discriminate differences in frequency as slight as one or two Hz, and we can recognize a complex waveform we heard only once twenty-four hours previously. But all these abilities can be degraded severely in less-than-perfect listening conditions, particularly by the presence of extraneous sounds. Determining how much our hearing is interfered with by unwanted sounds has been very important to the development of telephone and radio systems, as well as in tests of different theories of hearing.

One of the leaders of modern auditory research is Harvey Fletcher, formerly of the Bell Telephone Laboratories. Fletcher studied the degree to which broad-spectrum noise interferes with the ability to detect a tone, the frequency of which lies in the middle of the power spectrum of the noise. He reasoned that a tone produces an excitation pattern at only one region of the basilar membrane. Therefore, only those portions of the noise which excite that same region should interfere with our ability to detect the tone. To test this theory, he began with a very broadband masking noise (100 to 4000 Hz) and determined the just-detectable level of a 1000-Hz tone, which was masked by that noise. The tone, of course, had to be raised from its just-detectable level in the quiet, if it were to be detected in the presence of the noise. The amount of level change required is defined as the *amount of masking* (M). The *spectrum level* of the masking sound is generally measured in terms of its level per cycle or its average level in one-cycle wide bands. (The *overall level* of the noise is its level per cycle multiplied by its bandwidth, or in decibels, its spectrum level plus ten times the logarithm of its bandwidth.) Under the conditions of Fletcher's broadband masking experiment, the level of a 1000-Hz tone must be about 10 dB greater than the spectrum level of the noise for the tone to be detected. The next step in this experiment was to narrow the band of noise symmetrically around the frequency of the test tone. After each successive narrowing of the noise (reduction of its bandwidth and therefore of its overall level), the amount of masking was again measured. Fletcher found that the amount of masking did not change until the noise extended only 50 to 60 Hz above and below the tone. (This band-narrowing experiment is important to auditory theory; it is also perceptually impressive, even to a naive listener. The broadband noise sounds a great deal louder than the narrow-band noise, but a moment's listening can convince you that the two interfere with your hearing the tone by about the same amount.) Fletcher also reasoned that the band of noise critical to the masking of the tone was the part that excites the same cochlear region as the tone and that the width of this band must be another fundamental measure of the resolving power for frequency. This reasoning is further supported by the fact that the critical bandwidths vary with the test-tone frequency in roughly the same way as does the just-discriminable frequency difference, Δf. But the critical band is approximately 20 times the value of Δf at each frequency. When the masking experiment is conducted with different spectrum levels of noise, no change occurs in the ratio (difference in decibels) of the just-detectable tone level to the noise spectrum level. In other words, if the tone must be at 58 dB SPL to be heard above a 40 dB SPL spectrum-level noise, then it must be at 88 dB to be heard about a 70 dB SPL spectrum-level noise.

Another way of measuring the excitation pattern of a tone is by a tone-on-tone masking experiment. Here the question is, how much does a single-frequency tone mask all the other tones that might be presented to the listener. The answer is that the masking pattern of a tone is wider in frequency than Fletcher's critical bands, and it is definitely asymmetrical. Below the frequency of the masking tone, the amount of masking drops off rapidly. But above that frequency, the masking extends up much further (the exact amounts depend on the level of the masking tone). Recall the earlier discussion describing the traveling waves on the basilar membrane. This upward spread of masking is consistent with the fact that higher frequencies stimulate the portion of the membrane closest to the stapes, but may not affect portions closer to the apex.

Temporal masking and some other temporal phenomena. Since we are able to hear weaker sounds when they last longer, it might appear that the auditory system is an imprecise temporal analyzer. Nothing could be further from the truth. The system does act as an integrator (energy accumulator), capable of storing energy for as long as 150 to 200 msec, when we are trying to detect very faint sounds. But the same auditory system permits us to compare two 3-msec clicks and detect very slight differences between them. As Huggins and Licklider (1951) have suggested, the peripheral auditory system seems to encode the stimulus in several different ways and then send all of these transformations on to the decision stages of the nervous system. Decisions then can be based on whichever versions or combinations of versions of the input are most appropriate to the (detection, discrimination, or identification) task to be performed. This doesn't sound like a very parsimonious way to design a system, but then the best way to build in flexibility, adaptability, and resistance to perceptual confusion, may sometimes be to rank parsimony rather low among design criteria.

When we are attempting to "hear out" a faint sound, and no interfering sounds are present, other sounds nearby in time can still cause us trouble. To understand this problem, first recognize that we cannot be sensitive to any stimulus that does not have some extension in time and space. That is, we are sensitive to energy which impinges on our receptors only if that energy lasts for some brief time, ΔT, where ΔT is greater than zero and when that energy influences an area, ΔA, where ΔA is also greater than zero of the receptor's surface. In other words, the receptors act as summating or integrating systems whose responses are proportional to the amount of energy accumulated in ΔT time over ΔA area. We suggested that the system can appear to have different values of ΔT and ΔA, depending on the task we ask it to perform, but there must be a lower limit for each of these parameters. In the time domain, this limit has been called the *critical masking interval* and its operational definition is similar to that of Fletcher's critical bandwidth. The critical masking interval is that temporal extension of a masking sound, before and after a brief pulse, which is effective in masking that pulse. Research by Penner, Robinson, and Green (1972) has shown that energy arriving up to about 30 msec before and as late as 80 msec after a tone pulse can serve to mask it. Just as in the case of the bandwidth of excitation, when the task is to detect a faint sound, the region of integration appears to be greater than when we are trying to identify clearly audible sounds. If we could not discriminate among different temporal patterns of sounds as brief as 20 to 50 msec, we will see in a later section that we would have a difficult time understanding human speech.

RESPONSE PROCLIVITIES

As we said earlier, the objectively measurable aspects of hearing include sensory capability, or what you can do with your ears, and *response proclivities,* the characteristic responses people make to sounds when a variety of responses are clearly within the realm of their capability. The study of proclivities is primarily a matter of determining people's assertions about how things sound to them. The experiments, therefore, depend on methods different from those appropriate for studying capability. We have seen that capabilities are most accurately measured by some form of forced-choice psychophysical methods. Proclivity on the other hand is established by a listener telling us that a sound "seems" to have a certain pitch, or loudness, or to come from a certain point in the space around him. Proclivity measurement is thus very much a matter of determining the ways listeners use various words—and perhaps should be called *semantic psychophysics.*

Some words seem so essential to the description of sounds that in casual conversation we use them as though they were characteristics of the sounds rather than of the interaction between the sounds and the listeners. A sound is said to be high or low in *loudness, pitch, volume;* and these terms are sometimes given special status as the "psychological attributes" of sound to distinguish them from physical attributes. The concept of an attribute is an extremely sticky one and well worth careful examination, lest we use it carelessly. A *psychological attribute* of a sensory stimulus is an assumed dimension along which observers agree that the stimulus can vary. Thus if listeners are asked to rank sounds strictly according to their loudness, they can do so with fairly good agreement between listeners. But they can also rank the same sounds by their degrees of "annoyance," and the resulting rankings will be slightly different. They can even be asked to rank the sounds by their "purpleness" or by their "happiness" with modest degrees of inter-listener agreement. Why do we then call "loudness" an attribute of sound and not "annoyance," or "purpleness", or "happiness"? Two arbitrary reasons seem to explain our inclusion of some instructionally defined dimensions as attributes, while others are left off the list. One is that listeners agree with each other or are much more reliable in the way they use the attribute words in response to sounds than in the ways they use other words.

But be sure to realize that this does not mean that listeners agree perfectly about which of several sounds is the "loudest." They do not. Nor does it mean that there is no agreement about which sounds are the "happiest." Judged in terms of the degree of agreement among independent listeners, the attribute words simply rank higher than the nonattribute words. The other criterion is that the psychological attribute words are generally, although not always, related to a single physical dimension in the opinion of those who use the words. Thus "loudness" is often discussed as the psychological counterpart of sound intensity, and "pitch" as the counterpart of sound frequency. But as we shall see here, the psychological attributes of sounds are clearly different from their so-called physical counterparts, because the former can vary while the latter remain constant. In summary, psychological attributes of sounds are best understood as (1) words many listeners use in a consistent fashion to describe sounds, and (2) words whose use is closely, but imperfectly, correlated with one of the primary physical dimensions of sound. The only psychological attributes of sounds not consistent with this interpretation are those that have no closely correlated physical dimension, such as "volume" or "discord." This need not be a major problem, so long as one remembers that the psychological dimensions have no physical reality, but are merely properties inferred from behavioral responses to sounds.

Loudness. The most thoroughly measured of all of the psychological attributes of sounds is loudness. The relation between the physical characteristics of tones (sine waves) and their loudness, as reported by listeners, is described in Figure 15. The lowest curve in this figure, labeled "0," is both the minimum audible pressure and also approximately "zero loudness" (*approximately* because of the slight, but reliable, difference between the minimum pressure you can detect in a forced-choice procedure and the level of a sound you select as the weakest you believe you can hear). Imagine a horizontal line drawn across this figure at 60 dB SPL. Between 20 and 30 Hz the sounds along this line are inaudible. As we move from 30 Hz to about 4000 Hz, the sounds are farther and farther above the minimum pressure to which we are sensitive. A standard way of describing this fact is by the term *sensation level,* the number of decibels of a stimulus above the level which is barely detectable. (In older terms the words would be "above the threshold"; see Box 1.

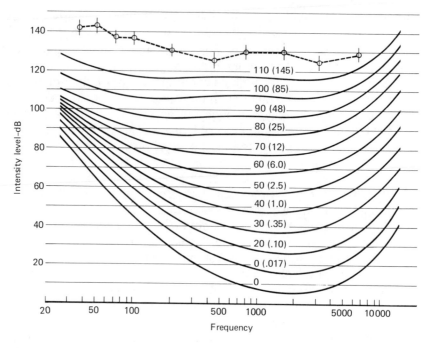

Figure 15. *Equal-loudness contours showing the level of tonal signals typically called equally loud. The zero contour is the minimum audible pressure, and the dashed line is an estimate of the "threshold of feeling." The first number on each curve is the number of decibels above the absolute threshold of the 1000-Hz tones that were used as the standard sounds (or their "sensation levels"). The second number is the scale value of the sounds in sones, an index of their sensational magnitude.* [Stevens and Davis. *Hearing: Its psychology and physiology, 1938. (New York: Wiley)*, 1938. Reprinted by permission.]

The sensation levels of the 60-dB SPL sounds thus range from 0 to about 55 dB. What does this mean about loudness? Nothing whatsoever, until we ask the listener about it. That is, there is no way of determining the loudness of a sound short of its defining operation, the judgment of a human listener. In practice, listeners are sometimes asked to adjust the level of a sound until it stands in some loudness ratio to another sound, for example, make one twice as loud as the other. Another common procedure is to ask the listener to give numerical estimates of the loudness of a sound: If we call this (first) sound a loudness of "10," what number would you assign to this (second) one? By methods such as these, we have learned that sounds along our 60-dB horizontal line do vary greatly in loudness, much as we would expect them to. It should now be clear that equal-intensity sounds are not equally loud, but neither are equal-sensa-

BOX 1

USE OF THE WORD "THRESHOLD"

Early in the history of sensory psychology, it was common to describe the just-detectable level of a stimulus as its "threshold." An analogy seemed to be drawn by the psychological use of this term between the results of psychophysical (behavioral) experiments and the all-or-none law of neurophysiology. It is now recognized that the level of a sound a listener claims to be just audible depends on both peripheral and central auditory mechanisms and on many more general factors, such as learning, attention, and memory. Therefore, behaviorally measured sensitivity probably should not be described by a term ("threshold") that suggests intimate relations between psychophysical measurement and any specific neural mechanisms. An alternative manner of speaking has been to use the phrase "just-detectable level" when referring to the results of psychophysical experiments by which we mean the level of a sound for which a trained listener can achieve some specific level of performance in a forced-choice psychophysical task. Just-detectable sound levels thus vary, depending on the percentage of correct responses selected as the criterion. Most commonly, the criterion for "just-detectable" levels is performance that is halfway between "chance" and "perfect," or 75 percent correct in a two-alternative, forced-choice task.

tion-level sounds. However these two incorrect alternatives are both nearly correct for particular levels of loudness. As shown in Figure 15, equal-loudness contours (determined by matching procedures) correspond to roughly equal sensation levels for the weakest sounds we can hear, but are much closer to having equal pressures in the region of 100 db SPL. Why loudness increases more rapidly at frequencies to which we are less sensitive is not obvious. An after-the-fact explanation might be that the top end of the scale is too loud to be tolerated and that it would be a useful protection from the effects of high-intensity noise for equal loudness to correspond roughly to equal destructiveness at such levels. But equal-intensity sounds are not equally destructive; so we must seek elsewhere for an explanation. Another explanation for the growth of loudness has been suggested by Warren (1963). He proposed that most sounds in our experience vary in level at our ears, but not at the sound source. In other words, most of our experience with differences in sound level results from movement closer to or further away from a sound source. We might then have essentially learned that "'double loudness" means the change in sound level produced by moving twice as close

BOX 2

S. S. STEVENS

S. S. Stevens (1906–1973) coined the term "psychoacoustics" and founded the extremely productive Psychoacoustics Laboratory at Harvard University. In this laboratory, many eminent experimental psychologists of the past 30 years learned their trade. Stevens' personal research during these years was primarily concerned with the way sensations seem to grow with increases in the intensity of a stimulus. He found that in every case, the estimated magnitude of a sensation increased in proportion to the stimulus intensity, raised to some power. The powers to which intensity must be raised are different for loudness, brightness, electrical shock, and so on. While Stevens' Power Law stands as an extremely useful empirical summary of one class of proclivity for many sensory modalities, its relation to other behavioral and physiological aspects of sensory processing remains to be determined. Stevens' work on the scaling of sensations is best described in a posthumous book, *Psychophysics,* which was published in 1975.

to the sound source. While an attractive proposition, this does not seem to be consistent with most experimental results, particularly those of the foremost psychoacoustician of his era, S. S. Stevens, which show that double loudness corresponds to an increase in sound pressure of roughly 10 dB. See Box 2.

Pitch. Pitch is the instructionally defined continuum or "attribute dimension" along which sound is said to vary when its frequency is changed. From the point of view of most western musical scales, equal increments in pitch mean equal logarithmic steps in fundamental frequency. Thus three octave steps starting at middle C correspond to 256, 512, and 1024 Hz; and musicians think of octaves as equal steps in pitch. However, judgments of pitch based on numerical magnitude estimates produce pitch scales that do not agree with the logarithmic rule, particularly at frequencies below about 500 Hz. At these lower frequencies, as shown in Figure 16 pitch judgments change less rapidly with frequency than is predicted by the logarithmic relation.

Two questions about pitch have been of recent concern to scientists, both having to do with how the peripheral auditory system processes sounds. One is, how is the place of maximum activity along the basilar membrane related to pitch judgments? The other is, what aspects of a sound other than its frequency are involved in de-

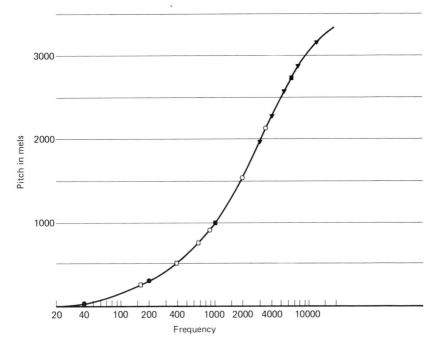

Figure 16. *The relation between tonal frequency and the subjective dimension called "pitch." The units on the subjective dimension were termed "mels" by S. S. Stevens. [From Stevens and Volkman. The relation of pitch to frequency, a revised scale.* American Journal of Psychology. *1940, 53, 329–353. Reprinted by permission of the University Illinois Press.]*

termining its pitch? Neither of these questions would make any sense, of course, if different places of maximum activity on the basilar membrane completely accounted for the pitches we hear. Here are two well-known experimental results showing that place theory cannot alone account for our perception of pitch. (1) If 600-, 800-, and 1000-Hz tones are simultaneously introduced to a listener's ear, he will report the corresponding pitches and also that he clearly hears the pitch of their common fundamental, 200 Hz. Further, the pitch associated with 200 Hz is not interfered with by a masking noise in the 200-Hz region, but only by a noise that masks the 600-, 800-, and 1000-Hz tones. The interpretation of this finding is that pitch depends not merely on the place of maximum activity, but on the overall periodicity of the waveform. (2) A similar result is found if a 1000-Hz tone is turned on and off at a rate of 100 times per second. Although there is no activity at the place on the basilar membrane normally associated with a 100 Hz, the pitch normally associated with a 100-Hz tone is reported, along with that of the 1000-Hz "carrier" frequency.

In addition to these examples, other well-established conditions exist in which listeners hear pitches that do not correspond to places of maximum activity on the basilar membrane. The weight of modern experimental evidence favors a theory of frequency resolution by the auditory system in which the temporal features of the input waveform are preserved in neural response patterns to a much greater degree than would be required by a simple "place theory." A speculation from the contemporary research literature is that the processing of mid to high frequencies requires that the associated places along the basilar membrane be intact and that the temporal features of the stimulus be encoded into a neural firing pattern. Lower frequencies, say below 500 Hz, may be encoded primarily in terms of the rates of neural responses rather than by the places of maximum activity. This view may be appreciated, at least at an unsophisticated level, by remembering that low frequencies lead to activity along the entire length of the basilar membrane, while high frequencies only lead to activity in restricted regions.

Timbre. This word, pronounced "timber" by most students of acoustics and "tanber" by musicians and some particularly well-dressed scientists, is used to represent the psychological response to the complexity of a waveform. Most often this word is used to refer to a waveform produced by a musical instrument. The sine waves or "pure tones" we have discussed thus far are normally produced by electronic oscillators, although a good round-lipped whistle is a close approximation.

Note: Technically minded readers may be aware of the extra qualification, that to be a "true" mathematically pure sine wave the sound would have to be of infinite duration. Sounds of less than infinite duration spread out in frequency. As the sound duration becomes very brief, this "spreading" becomes very pronounced. A good approximation to this effect, for sine waves, is given by the formula,

$$B.W. = \frac{1}{T}.$$

The bandwidth ($B.W.$), expressed in Hz, is approximately the reciprocal of the duration (T) expressed in seconds. Thus a 1-msec tone actually has a bandwidth of about 1000 Hz, a 10-msec tone a bandwidth of about 100 Hz, and a 100-msec tone a bandwidth of about 10 Hz. Since our discussions here primarily concern sounds that are one-quarter second long or longer, this "frequency splatter" is not very important. But clearly it is a considerable worry to those who work with very brief sounds.

In the case of most musical instruments, the special quality of their sound, apart from loudness or pitch, is determined by their character-istic pattern of overtones. The pitch is determined by the fundamental frequency at which a string or a column of air vibrates, but the timbre is determined by the relative intensities of the "harmonics" or "over-tones" of the fundamental frequency. *Harmonics* and *overtones* are different names for the simple multiples of the fundamental fre-quency. (They differ in that the first harmonic is considered to be the fundamental itself, and thus the second harmonic is the first over-tone.) For example, the line spectra of a clarinet, a violin, and a piano are shown in Figure 17. The violin and clarinet are both playing notes whose pitch is that of the 200-Hz fundamental. But the different quali-ties (timbres) of the two instruments are determined by their mechan-ical structure, which in turn determines the relative levels of the vari-ous harmonics. Small differences in these patterns can mean that one violin is of great value while another makes the school music teacher turn pale. In the past 20 years, the mathematical description of stringed instruments has progressed to the point that an instrument with virtually any desired timbre can be produced.

There are many, many varieties of response proclivity which we have been unable to include in this discussion. Sounds are annoy-ing in varying degrees; they are concordant or discordant (seem to complement or fight with each other when played together); they are even said to have emotional character. One word of caution is sug-gested for the reader interested in these matters. Do not be too quick to assume that any particular proclivity is either simply a learned re-sponse or that it reflects some fundamental aspect of the processing of sounds by the nervous system. Being too quick to draw either assumption has been a source of embarrassment to many reputable scientists.

LOCALIZING SOUNDS IN SPACE

Readers who have not tried the demonstration described in the Introduction to this unit should go back and experiment with it before reading this. It is hard to appreciate your own remarkable ability to identify the location of a sound source until you have tried it with your eyes closed. Under normal circumstances, we tend to blend our sen-sory experiences together. We do not say to ourselves, "I heard a sound of a particular sort, and I also saw the ball leave the bat." Rather we say, "He hit the ball." Judgments about our environment

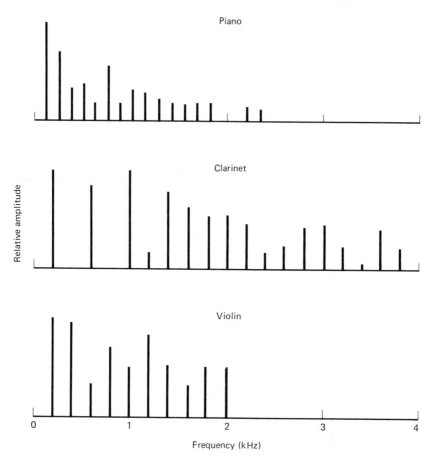

Figure 17. *The acoustic spectra of clarinet, violin, and piano. The pitch of these sound sources is primarily determined by the lowest frequency component in their spectrum. The remaining components determine the subjective quality of the sound, or its "timbre."*

are mainly concerned with what happens out there, not with how our sensory apparatus is working (unless, of course, it malfunctions). We respond to the world with the overall integrated information from all our senses, shaped or modulated by our previous hunches about how the world most likely is. This is an efficient way for us to function. After all, we need to know what is going on around us, not how we know it. But this can mean that introspection is a poor way to learn the details of sensory psychology. For this purpose, we need controlled experiments, even as simple as the one in the Introduction.

If you have two normal ears, you should have been able to identify the hand that snapped its fingers with very few errors, if any. What actually are the limits of this ability? Figure 18 shows the approximate

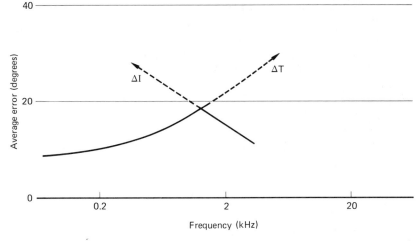

Figure 18. *Idealization of the relation between the frequency of a sound source and the average localization error, in degrees, made by a human listener, for sources located 15 to 20 degrees off of the median plane. The dashed lines illustrate the ability to localize using only differences in interaural arrival time (ΔT) or in interaural intensity (ΔI) as the localization cue.*

minimum discriminable angles, in degrees, for various frequencies of pure tones. Illustrated in this figure is one of two peculiar facts of auditory localization: you do it best at the high and low frequencies. Most other auditory capabilities are maximal in the mid-frequency range, where the human is most sensitive to sound. The other peculiarity of auditory localization is that it is the only auditory capability that, like stereoscopic vision, requires the two receptor organs to work together.

Research and theory on auditory localization has made enviable progress in the past 30 years. It is a case where all three fundamental questions of sensory science have been at least partly answered and where the answers are in good agreement with each other: (1) psychophysical experiments have shown what we can and cannot do in the way of localizing sounds. (2) Physical analysis of the waveforms has shown what the cues are by which we accomplish this localization. (3) And most recently, the anatomy and physiology of the portions of the auditory system responsible for localization are beginning to be understood.

PHYSICAL CUES FOR LOCALIZING SOUNDS

Since we cannot localize sounds unless both ears are working, it has long been clear that interaural differences in the sounds we hear must be the relevant cues. The sounds at the two ears differ in two ways when the sound source is located to one side of the median plane (the plane, as we said earlier, that divides one's head into its two most symmetrical halves). Sound must travel further to get to one ear than the other; so there is a difference (ΔT) in the arrival time of the sounds at the two ears. This difference depends on the rate of the conduction of sound through the air, which is the same for all frequencies. The ΔT associated with a particular sound source is thus independent of frequency. If one ear is "turned away" from a sound source, the sound must "bend" around the head to get to that ear; it cannot merely travel along a straight line between the source and the ear. Sounds "bend" around objects only if the objects are small relative to the wavelength (distance traveled in one period) of the sound. High frequencies thus tend to go right on past the ear on the far side of the head, while low frequencies tend to bend around the head and stimulate the far-side ear. Another way of saying this is that the higher the frequency of a sound, the more it tends to cast a "sound shadow." If more sound intensity gets to one ear than the other, there will be an intensity difference (ΔI) between them. And for a particular position of the sound source, the value of ΔI will be greater for high frequencies than for low. For example, if a sound source is located 15 degrees away from the median plane, at 300 Hz, ΔI will be about 1 dB; at 1000 Hz, about 4 dB; and at 10,000 Hz, about 6 dB.

PSYCHOPHYSICAL FACTS OF LOCALIZATION

The basic facts of our ability to locate the sources of tones were shown in Figure 18. But these data, collected with a loudspeaker as the source, do not tell us whether the listeners were relying on ΔI or ΔT or a combination of both to make their judgments. This question required that experimenters devise a way to vary one of these cues while the other stayed constant. This is actually simple, because with earphones and an appropriate electronic circuit we can vary ΔI and ΔT independently. Experiments with earphones show that at low frequencies we depend almost entirely on ΔT (or phase difference if the sound is a continuing wave). This is not surprising, since at low frequencies there simply is not much ΔI for us to rely on. At high frequencies we mainly depend on ΔI. We can say, after the fact, that this too is fortunate. At high frequencies, the length of one cycle of the waveform is short relative to the head. This means that determining whether there is a relative phase lead or phase lag is ambiguous when one ear may actually be several cycles ahead or behind the other. The fact of worst localization performance at mid-frequencies is thus understandable, since we rely on ΔI at high frequencies and ΔT at low frequencies; but both cues have reduced effectiveness at mid-frequencies.

Much of our auditory localization takes place inside buildings rather than in the acoustic simplicity of wheat fields or trapezes sus-

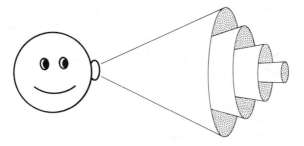

Figure 19. *A set of "cones of confusion" idealized for a spherical head. The surface of each cone represents all those points in space at which sound sources would yield identical interaural differences in both intensity and arrival times. These surfaces are members of a family, the extremes of which are the median plane and a line drawn directly through the two ears.*

pended from balloons. Walls, floors, and ceilings cause sound waves to be reflected until the patterns are difficult to predict even by a well-trained physicist; there are just too many variables involved. Incidentally, exactly how the marvelous acoustics of European churches built in the Middle Ages was achieved is still a bit of a mystery. Some frustrated modern architects have suggested that they must have torn down the ones with poor acoustical properties.) But despite the multiple paths taken by sounds to reach our ears in a "live" room (one with a high proportion of efficient acoustic reflectors among its exposed surfaces), we generally can still tell where the source is located. This stems from a very convenient feature of auditory localization, called the "precedence effect." When several similar waveforms reach our ears in close succession, we locate the sound in terms of the direction from which the first waveform came. Not only that, but we also tend to blend in the later arriving waveforms in our perception and do not say we have heard a sequence of sounds at all. Only when the delay between the waveforms is greater than about 20 msec do we begin to hear them as separate sounds.

Although the ability to localize sound sources is good, it does have some shortcomings. The average errors in Figure 18 do not include front-back confusions. Consider two sound sources on the median plane. One is directly in front of you, the other directly behind you. The ΔT and ΔI are both zero, for both sounds. There is no clear way you could tell which direction the sound was coming from. In fact, all of the sound sources lying on the surface of any cone—the apex of which is in one ear and the major axis is the line passing through the two ears, as shown in Figure 19—yield the same values of ΔT and ΔI. The family of cones illustrated in the figure are thus known as "cones of confusion." We seem to decide where on the surface of a cone of confusion a sound comes from partly by using common sense and partly by an extra feature of our ears. The first is simply that we can usually bet that if someone is yelling at us, he is on the ground, not floating in midair. (Try calling to someone from a second or third-story window. The listener will nearly always look to the two ground-level points on the appropriate cone of confusion; and you will often have to say, "Hey, up here!" before he will find you.) The second is that the external ear (the pinna) casts a slightly greater shadow for high-frequency sounds, thus changing the spectrum of sounds arriving from the rear. Only if you know the spectrum to expect, of course, can you use this subtle cue. With pure tones it is of no value whatsoever.

ANATOMY AND PHYSIOLOGY
OF AUDITORY LOCALIZATION

Animal studies have shown that the auditory cortex is probably required for precise localization of sound sources and that the actual comparison of the neural effects from the two ears occurs at a much lower level of the nervous system. The precision of localization shows that we can discriminate differences of arrival time as small as 20–30 microseconds. Professor Lloyd Jeffress, the father of modern studies of binaural hearing, recognized that such precise time discriminations must mean that the interaural comparison takes place early in the auditory system, for neural events become diffuse in time the further they go in the system. He proposed, in 1948, that the neural comparison must take place in a series of "neural delay lines," like those pictured in Figure 20. Neural impulses begun at the two ears cause a post-synaptic cell (on the side of the synapses toward the higher portion of the nervous system) to fire only when their arrival at the synapse approximately coincides in time; the whole array is termed a neural coincidence detector. What this theoretical neural circuit is supposed to accomplish is a recoding of various values of ΔT into various places of activity in the nervous system. (This goal is consistent with a principle proposed many years ago by a thoughtful psychologist, E. G. Boring. Boring's idea was that if we can discriminate between two stimuli, they most likely elicit neural action in different places.) Several years after Jeffress postulated this neural decoding circuit, other scientists discovered single cells in the olivary nucleus that respond only to interaural delays of certain minimum values of ΔT. This appeared to be strong evidence in favor both of the neural-coincidence detector model and also for Jeffress's idea that the comparison between the two ears' responses must come extremely early in the nervous system. The story is not yet complete, however, since the interaurally sensitive cells tend to respond to a wide range of values of ΔT beyond the minimum required. This im-

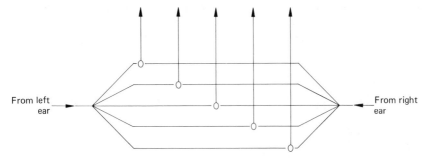

Figure 20. *A theoretical neural delay line of the type proposed by Jeffress to account for the translation of differences in the interaural arrival time of sounds into differences in the place of major neural activity. The Os represent the synaptic junctions at which neural connections from the two ears converge on a common higher order neuron. If the higher order neurons will only respond when the right and left inputs converge upon them simultaneously, then such a "coincidence detecting network" would be consistent with many of the facts of binaural hearing. [After L. A. Jeffress. A place theory of sound localization.* Journal of Comparative and Physiological Psychology. *1948, 41, 35–39.]*

plies some extra circuitry beyond that proposed by Jeffress, probably involving a form of inhibition. The work continues.

MASKING-LEVEL DIFFERENCES

Before leaving the subject of binaural hearing, we should touch on one additional phenomenon closely related to auditory localization. If sounds arriving at the two ears with different values of ΔT lead to different places of activity in the binaural portions of the nervous system, this would have an interesting consequence. Sounds with the same ΔT should interfere with (mask) each other much more than sounds with different ΔTs. In practical terms, this means a person talking to you might not be heard if a noisy machine were behind him, but might be heard if he moved so that he and the machine were on different cones of confusion. Many experiments by Jeffress and his students, and others, have shown this prediction to be accurate. A noise source on the median plane is 12–14 dB more effective in masking a tone on the median plane than a tone that is delayed by one-half cycle at one ear relative to the other. The enhanced performance in the *antiphasic* (noise and tone in different phase relations at the two ears) as compared to the *homophasic* (noise and tone in the same phase relations at the two ears) condition is called a *masking level difference* (MLD). Since the MLD depends mainly on ΔT and since this is a useful cue only at low frequencies (below 1000 Hz), it seems understandable that MLDs are greatly reduced at high frequencies. Every now and then a single well-established fact seems to lead to better understanding of a large number of other issues, and the MLD may turn out to have been such a keystone.

SPEECH: THE MOST IMPORTANT SOUND

The production and perception of speech is not simply an innate characteristic of human beings. But the fact that human beings do acquire these abilities sets them apart from all other living creatures. Over the past 40 years, numerous attempts have been made to raise other animals, particularly chimpanzees, in a speaking environment. Some chimps have learned as many as one hundred words, using either sign language or symbols placed on a board. But their ability to use the language is so restricted that some theorists refuse to call their acquired skill speech. Children reared for their first few years in a nonspeaking environment never learn normal speech. There have been about 20 moderately well-documented cases of feral children (that is, children who have been raised by or with animals rather than humans). When found and returned to a human environment, these children have not acquired normal human speech. The combination of evidence from animals which cannot be taught to speak and feral children who do not learn to speak suggests that speech is an acquired skill, which can only be learned by humans. The physiological and anatomical structures required for speech also support the view that speech is special to people. On the production side we come equipped with a flexible vocal tract, capable of producing a very complex catalog of sounds. The central neural control of speech perception and production appears, in most people, to be located in the left cerebral hemisphere. This unique asymmetrically placed "center" has also been interpreted as proof that the human alone has the necessary structures to become a speaking creature.

It has often been suggested that thought is nothing but subvocal speech. This argument is too complex to review here. Evidence has not shown the muscles of the vocal tract to be particularly active while we are thinking. But the shorthand representation of many things by one word clearly should give an advantage to a thinker who knows a language compared to one who does not. The types of confusions one makes in trying to retrieve information from memory show that speaking people systematically store information both in terms of a word's sounds and also according to its meaning. The word you incorrectly "remember" may either sound like the correct one or it may have a similar or related meaning. Research in what is currently called "cognitive" psychology has produced evidence that whether thinking is merely subvocal language (probably it is not), it definitely is very much related to the thinker's knowledge of language and his habitual language patterns.

PHYSICAL NATURE OF SPEECH

Our main concern here is how we hear speech, and for this purpose we need to understand the physical nature of speech. The sounds that come from the mouth consist of two major classes: voiced and unvoiced. *Voiced* sounds begin with air pressure from the lungs being forced against the membranous bands of the vocal folds (true vocal cords) of the larynx. These folds act as a valve, and during a voiced sound, they open and close at a rapid rate. The opening and closing allow "puffs" or pulses of air to pass through into the throat and mouth. The rate of opening and closing of the vocal folds determines the fundamental frequency of the voice. Sound waves are in turn propagated by the air pulses, and these sound waves cause the cavities of the throat and mouth to resonate at frequencies determined by their size and shape. The spectrum of a voiced-speech sound consists, like that of any other periodic sound, of its fundamental frequency, plus various amounts of each of many higher harmonics (integral multiples) of the fundamental frequency. The relative sound levels of each of the higher harmonics depends on the shape of the vocal cavities. The vocal cavities consist of the total volume of the nose, mouth, and throat. The throat and mouth volume is divided into two major sections, the size of which depends on the position of the tongue. The tongue position is therefore the major determiner of the size of the resonant cavities and thus of the form of the voice spectrum for voiced sounds. All vowels are voiced sounds, and the role of the tongue in producing them can easily be felt in your own mouth. Simply open your mouth slightly and say a prolonged *a* as in father. Then gradually shift to *e* as in yes, and finally to *ee* as in three. These vowels can be produced easily, even though the fundamental frequency, jaw position, and the lip closure remain constant. Other vowels require that the lip closure be changed, but we will not attempt to list the positions of the articulators for each of them.

In the voice spectrum there can be as many as six resonant "peaks" produced by the main vocal cavities and the smaller spaces around them. This means that the harmonics (multiples of the fundamental) in the vicinity of each of these peaks are passed from the mouth, while the other harmonics are relatively suppressed or impeded. A simple analogy to this process is the excitation of a slide trombone by the vibration of the lips at the mouthpiece. The interrupted airflow propagates a sound wave into the instrument at the frequency (the fundamental) at which you vibrated your lips. In the output of the instrument, various harmonics are emphasized, depending on the size of its resonant cavity, which you control with the slide.

The fundamental frequency of men's speech is about 130 Hz, that of women about 220 Hz, and about 250 Hz for young children. The lower three resonances, called *formants,* range between 270 and 3000 Hz for men, 300 and 3300 Hz for women, and 370 and 3700 Hz for children. It is the relative frequencies of the first three formants that produces the characteristic timbre of each vowel. Figure 21 shows a diagram called a speech spectrogram. Frequency is plotted on the ordinate, time on the abscissa; and the relative intensity of each frequency in the speech spectrum is shown by the darkness of the display. The lowest dark horizontal bar is the fundamental; those above it are the first three formants. Notice how the frequencies of the formants change as the utterance moves from one vowel to the next.

Consonants can be partly voiced, like the vowels; but they are often *unvoiced,* that is, do not begin with a vocal-fold produced fundamental frequency. Instead, some consonants are produced by opening the vocal fold continuously to produce a steady flow of air. Pushed through a narrow passage this air flow produces a broadband noise (like steam escaping). The spectrum of this noise can be shaped by the lips and tongue, as in producing the *fricative* sounds, *sh* and *f.* Other consonants, called *stops* or *stop consonants* are produced by blocking all air flow and then releasing it in a single sudden "puff," as in the case of *p* or *b.* The former is called an *unvoiced,* the latter a *voiced,* consonant. Try saying them in isolation and you will see why.

Figure 21 shows the spectrum of some of the consonants. In general, there is far less total sound energy in the consonants than in the vowels; and the consonants have more high frequencies in them than do the vowels.

PERCEIVING SPEECH

To "hear" speech requires that we analyze a rapidly changing complex waveform, the spectrum of which ranges from 200 to 4000 or 5000 Hz (including the lower six formants, not just the three thought to be of major importance). This is some order. No one has yet been able to build an electronic device capable of doing it in "real time," but our auditory system manages quite well. In fact, we can understand speech, even if it is severely degraded, by filtering out all but the frequencies between 300 and 2500 to 3000 Hz. The quality seems a bit "thin" when this is done, but the speech sounds remain intelligible. In fact, intelligibility is preserved even when speech is severely distorted by deleting periodic sections of it or by chopping all of its energy peaks. In general, our speech reception

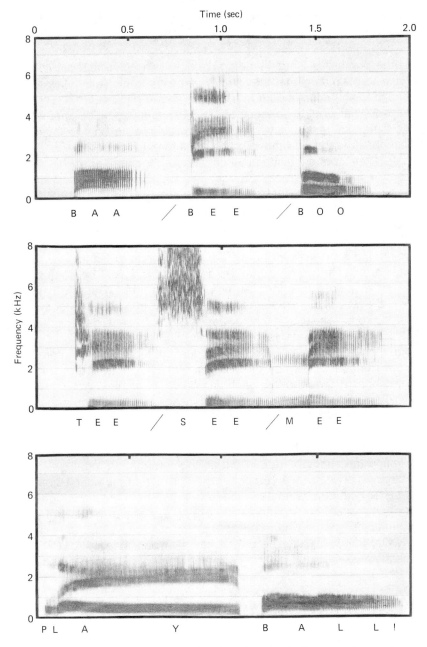

Figure 21. *Speech spectrogram showing changes in the speech spectrum over time. The darkness of the spectrogram represents the relative intensities of each of the major spectral components. The vowels are characterized by frequency bands called* formants. *The consonants are most often brief bursts of noise. [Courtesy of R. Monsen, Central Institute for the Deaf.]*

system seems to be designed like any good communication scheme. It can take much punishment and still get the message through.

Some modern theories of speech perception propose that part of the process of understanding speech is through *analysis by synthesis*. This means that the listener first says to himself, "How would I have to shape my mouth to make the sound I just heard?" Then he says, "What would I be trying to say if I shaped my mouth that way?" This may seem a bit awkward, and of course no one believes the listener is literally aware of such an inferential process. But some data from speech discrimination and recognition experiments do seem consistent with such a scheme, and it is an excellent way of coping with the fact that speech waveforms come in a virtually infinite variety. We the listeners seem to make use of our advance knowledge that only a certain catalog of acoustic symbols are being attempted by the speakers. It is also true that we make considerable use of the word-to-word predictability of speech to reduce our errors in hearing. The words "Paul" and "ball" can easily be confused if they are spoken in isolation in a noisy environment. But few listeners would ever have a problem with them when they were preceded by the words, "The boy's name was _____"; or "The boy hit the _____." Remember Helmholtz's two main propositions about hearing—that it depends on both the acoustical input and on inferences drawn unconsciously by the listener. Research has shown that the inferences drawn about speech can be very complex. We draw from our knowledge of the immediate acoustic input, the words that immediately preceded that input, the topic of the conversation, the speaker's fundamental frequencies and typical formant values, and what we have seen his *articulators* (mainly his lips and tongue) do in forming the sounds. We can put all this information together—without being aware of the components—to arrive at the conclusion that a certain utterance has been made with a certain emotional tone, by a certain speaker. An impressive example of this synthesis of cues sometimes occurs when you answer the telephone and are able to identify the caller after he or she has said only "Hello," or "Hi," or merely made a throat-clearing sound in preparation for speaking.

HEARING IMPAIRMENT

The ability to hear is most valued when it is contrasted with failure of this sense. Congenital deafness, unless extensive special training is undertaken during the language-learning years, makes it impossible for the deaf person to communicate with most of his fellowmen. An impoverished vocabulary can result in isolation, not only from the social community of most of humankind, but also from its cultural attainments, history, literature, and politics. Even deafness that occurs later in life, if it is severe, can result in gradual deterioration of our speech and often causes the deaf adult to withdraw into social isolation.

TYPES OF HEARING IMPAIRMENT

The two major classes of hearing impairment are, (1) that which interferes with sound energy before it is transduced into neural impulses, and (2) that in which the neural activity itself is degraded. The first is called *conductive deafness,* the second *nerve deafness.* The simplest generalization about these two forms of impairment is that there are many ways of correcting most conductive disorders and almost no satisfactory solutions to the nerve-based ones. Conductive deafness can result from a waxy buildup in the ear canal, which many readers have certainly experienced and had corrected by a physician flushing the canal with water. Conductive deafness of a more serious nature involves a decrease in the efficiency of energy transmission through the middle ear (newest evidence suggests that it may also result from a stiffening of the basilar membrane), but this too generally responds to medical or surgical treatment. The only generally accepted treatment for nerve deafness of the cochlea or of higher parts of the auditory system is a hearing aid. These devices seldom restore hearing to the quality one would hope for, although they can produce worthwhile improvements in many cases.

The main functional characteristic of conductive deafness is that it often results in a fairly constant loss of sensitivity at all frequencies. Increasing the level of the sound introduced to the ear returns hearing to essentially normal acuity.

NERVE DEAFNESS

Nerve deafness comes in many varieties, reflecting the great number of places at which the neural portions of the auditory system can malfunction. The most common form of nerve deafness is one in which sensitivity to sounds above 2000 or 3000 Hz is moderately or severely reduced. The more severe this form of nerve deafness, the lower the frequency limit of audible sounds. When sound above 2000 Hz is inaudible, there will be serious confusion between consonants. When sound above 1000 Hz is inaudible, both vowels and consonants may be unintelligible. But as we mentioned in the discussion on speech, so many cues are used in understanding a conversation that considerable deafness can exist before it prevents communication or even before the listener is aware of it.

A major difference between conductive and nerve deafness is in the way loudness grows with intensity. In conductive deafness, all sounds are reduced in their loudness exactly by the amount of the hearing loss. Thus if a patient acquires a 30-dB conductive loss, a 90-dB SPL sound will be as loud as a 60-dB SPL sound normally is. But a patient with a 30-dB nerve deafness may hear a 90-dB SPL sound at its normal loudness level. This fact of nerve deafness reducing sensitivity, but not changing the loudness of sounds that can be heard, is called *recruitment*. Nerve deafness is sometimes called "recruiting deafness," although some auditory neural problems are not characterized by this rapid growth of loudness as a function of sound level.

CAUSES AND PREVENTION OF NERVE DEAFNESS

Nerve deafness can be an inherited defect, it can be caused by infections, it can result from exposure to intense noise, and many people develop it in old age without any clearly identifiable cause. Rubella (German Measles) during pregnancy is a prime cause of congenital deafness, which can be avoided by vaccination before pregnancy. Unlike most other dangerous conditions to which we can expose ourselves, there are no clear warning signals with intense noise. The noise level at which auditory pain is felt, according to most experts, is 20–30 dB above the level that can cause permanent damage to the fine structures of the cochlea. As the system is damaged, it becomes less sensitive. After a factory worker has been exposed to an intense noise for a few weeks he may report that, "it doesn't seem so bad anymore; I must have gotten used to it." Earplugs and ear defenders are effective protective devices. It is important to remember that if you must hear a warning signal above an intense noise, you may be able to hear it as well wearing ear plugs as without them. This is because the *signal-to-noise ratio* can be the same with or without the earplugs.

COMMUNICATING WITH HEARING-IMPAIRED PEOPLE

First, keep reminding yourself that the degraded, perhaps slurred, speech quality of deaf people who have learned to speak does not mean that they have intellectual deficits. To speak for years and never hear the result can almost inevitably lead to so-called deaf-speech quality. Second, the deaf person who speaks also reads lips, so face him or her directly when you speak. Try to position yourself in the room so that your face is well illuminated. Third, make your speech as predictable as the message you want to convey will permit. As we said earlier, understanding speech is a blend of hearing and predicting, so the less your listener can predict, the more he must hear, or lip-read. Making your speech predictable means doing several things you can discover by practice. You should avoid odd words and phrases and abrupt changes of topic.

Many congenitally deaf people have not learned to speak except through sign language. With them, you must be patient and write notes or use gestures or pantomime if the message will permit.

There is a long-standing controversy among those in the field of the education of the deaf about the relative values of teaching sign language versus teaching lipreading and oral speech. The arguments are too lengthy to pursue here, but one generally acknowledged fact should be mentioned. It is that most congenitally deaf people can be taught to speak intelligibly if they have systematic instruction begun at an early age. This means that most so-called deaf and dumb people do not lack the mechanisms to produce speech, but that they have not learned to use them.

NOISE AS AN ECOLOGICAL PROBLEM

Noise levels in our cities are increasing by 1 dB or so each year. We have not yet come anywhere near the levels where this is a serious health hazard. But most people agree that the quality of life has been reduced by the constant presence of high levels of background noise. The solutions of this problem, like the answers to many other ecological conditions, may cost more than we are willing to spend. Noise control ordinances may require large expenditures by some factories and small extra costs by the homeowner who buys a quieter lawnmower or skimobile. But it costs many times more to correct noisy conditions after the buildings or machines responsible for them have been built than during the original building. If we want a quieter environment, we have the technology available to produce it.

FINAL COMMENT

Auditory perception, as Helmholtz recognized so clearly, is a complex process in which the prediction of what we ought to be hearing is inextricably blended, in consciousness or in the behavioral response, with the effects of the sounds actually impinging on our auditory apparatus. This does not mean that hearing is special, but rather that it is as creative an experience as seeing, or smelling, or feeling. The task of future scientists is to systematically determine the contributions of the acoustic stimulus, of short and long-term memory, and of the innate properties of the human auditory system, to perception of the complex sounds of our environment, including especially speech and music. Research and theory described in this unit represent the first century of auditory science, which dealt primarily with tones, noise bursts, and clicks. Investigations of the patterns of responses elicited by those elementary stimuli have provided a firm foundation for the study of the sounds the system is probably designed to hear.

REFERENCES

Boring, E. G. *Sensation and perception in the history of experimental psychology.* New York: Appleton-Century-Crofts, 1942.
————. *A history of experimental psychology.* 2d ed. New York: Appleton-Century-Crofts, 1950.
Davis, H., and Silverman, S. R. *Hearing and deafness.* 3d ed. New York: Holt, Rinehart and Winston, 1970.
Egan, J. P. *Signal detection theory and ROC analysis.* New York, Academic Press, 1975.
Galambos, R. Microelectrode studies on the auditory nervous system. *Ann. Otol. Rhinol. & Laryngol.* 1957, *66,* 503–505.
Green, D. M. and Swets, J. A. *Signal detection theory and psychophysics.* New York: John Wiley and Sons, 1966; revised ed. Huntington, New York, Robert E. Krieger Publishing Co. 1974.
Harris, J. D. Pitch perception. *J. Acoust. Soc. Am.* 1952, *24,* 750–755.
Henning, G. B. Frequency discrimination of random-amplitude tones. *J. Acoust. Soc. Am.* 1966, *39,* 336–339.
Huggins, W. H., and Licklider, J. C. R. Place mechanisms of auditory frequency analysis. *J. Acoust Soc. Am.* 1951, *23,* 290–299.
Jeffress, L. A. A place theory of sound localization. *J. of Comp. & Physiol. Psychol.* 1948, *41,* 35–39.
Kiang, N. Y.-S. *Discharge patterns of single fibers in the cat's auditory nerve.* Research Monogr. No. 35. Cambridge, Mass.: MIT Press, 1965.
Miller, G. A. The magical number seven, plus or minus two: Some limits on our capacity for processing information. *Psychol. Rev.* 1956, *63,* 81–97.
Miller, J. D. The effects of noise on people. *J. Acoust. Soc. Am.* 1974, *56,* 729–764.
————, and Tanis, D. C. Recognition memory for common sounds. *Psychon. Sci.* 1971, *23,* 307–308.
Penner, M. J., Robinson, C. E., and Green, D. M. The critical masking interval. *J. Acoust. Soc. Am.* 1972, *52,* 1661–1668.
Pierce, J. R., and David, E. E. *Man's world of sound.* Garden City, New York: Doubleday, 1958.
Rose, J. E., Brugge, J. F., Anderson, D. J., and Hind, J. E. Phase-locked response to low-frequency tones in single auditory nerve fibers of the squirrel monkey. *J. Neurophysiol.* 1967, *30,* 769–793.
Stevens, S. S. *Psychophysics* (G. Stevens, ed) New York: John Wiley & Sons, 1975.
————, and Davis, H. *Hearing: Its psychology and physiology.* New York: John Wiley & Sons, 1938.
————, and Volkmann, J. The relation of pitch to frequency: A revised scale. *Am. J. Psychol.* 1940, *53,* 329–353.
Warren, R. M. Are loudness judgments based on distance estimates? *J. Acoust. Soc. Am.* 1963, *35,* 613(L).
————, and Warren, R. P. *Helmholtz on perception, its physiology and development.* New York: John Wiley & Sons, 1968.
Watson, C. S. Psychophysics. In Wolman, B., ed., *Handbook of general psychology.* New York: Prentice Hall, 1973.
Watson, C. S., Franks, J., and Hood, D. M. Detection of tones in the absence of external masking noise. *J. Acoust. Soc. Am.* 1972, *52,* 633–643.
Whitefield, I. C. Centrifugal control mechanism of the auditory pathway. In A. V. S. de Renck and Julie Knight, Eds., *Hearing mechanism in vertebrates.* CIBA Foundation Symposium. London: J. & A. Churchill, 1968.